CW00797211

Atlas of mammals in Britain

ITE research publication no. 6

H R Arnold

LONDON: HMSO

Natural Environment Research Council

© Crown copyright 1993
  Applications for reproduction should be made to HMSO
  Second impression 1994

ISBN 0 11 701667 5

Cover design by Richard Thewliss

The Institute of Terrestrial Ecology (ITE) is a component research organisation within the Natural Environment Research Council. The Institute is part of the Terrestrial and Freshwater Sciences Directorate, and was established in 1973 by the merger of the research stations of the Nature Conservancy with the Institute of Tree Biology. It has been at the forefront of ecological research ever since. The six research stations of the Institute provide a ready access to sites and to environmental and ecological problems in any part of Britain. In addition to the broad environmental knowledge and experience expected of the modern ecologist, each station has a range of special expertise and facilities. Thus, the Institute is able to provide unparallelled opportunities for long-term, multidisciplinary studies of complex environmental and ecological problems.

ITE undertakes specialist ecological research on subjects ranging from micro-organisms to trees and mammals, from coastal habitats to uplands, from derelict land to air pollution. Understanding the ecology of different species of natural and man-made communities plays an increasingly important role in areas such as monitoring ecological aspects of agriculture, improving productivity in forestry, controlling pests, managing and conserving wildlife, assessing the causes and effects of pollution, and rehabilitating disturbed sites.

The Institute's research is financed by the UK Government through the science budget, and by private and public sector customers who commission or sponsor specific research programmes. ITE's expertise is also widely used by international organisations in overseas collaborative projects.

The results of ITE research are available to those responsible for the protection, management and wise use of our natural resources, being published in a wide range of scientific journals, and in an ITE series of publications. The Annual Report contains more general information.

The Biological Records Centre is operated by ITE, as part of the Environmental Information Centre, and receives financial support from the Joint Nature Conservation Committee. It seeks to help naturalists and research biologists to co-ordinate their efforts in studying the occurrence of plants and animals in the British Isles, and to make the results of these studies available to others.

H R Arnold
Environmental Information Centre
Biological Records Centre
Institute of Terrestrial Ecology
Monks Wood
Abbots Ripton
HUNTINGDON, Cambs PE17 2LS
04873 (Abbots Ripton) 381

Contents

Introduction

The surveys

The Mammal Society began their survey of British mammals in 1965, in co-operation with the Biological Records Centre (BRC). The British Deer Society began a similar survey of deer in 1967, and deer records gathered by the Mammal Society were passed to the Deer Society. A set of provisional maps for mammals including deer was published in Mammal Review in 1971 (Corbet 1971) which included all records received by the end of 1970, and additional deer maps were published by the British Deer Society in 1974, covering the period 1967–72. The maps published in 1970 were admittedly very provisional, but the intention was to stimulate further recording and to encourage the 'filling in' of the blank areas. This was successful and a further set of provisional maps was produced in 1978 (Arnold 1978) which again stimulated further recording. In 1984 a third set of maps was produced (Arnold 1984) in an effort to get the more obvious omissions remedied, but this set had less effect than the other two versions. While the general distribution survey was being carried out, other surveys of mammals, mainly single species surveys, were being organised. Some, like the harvest mouse survey and the dormouse survey, were organised almost entirely by the Mammal Society, but in later years surveys were designed and financed by other organisations such as the Nature Conservancy Council (NCC) and the Vincent Wildlife Trust. Some of these later surveys were carried out by an employed surveyor, looking at a stratified sample of grid squares, and collecting comprehensive ecological information on sites.

The records

Records of mammals can be gained in many different ways; not only are mammals seen, but they can be heard (foxes, deer) or smelt (foxes). They leave tracks, faeces and feeding signs; they dig holes or build nests. Many are killed by other animals (including man) and their remains are found in bird pellets, carnivore droppings and on gamekeepers' gibbets. Many fall victim to the motor car, and occasionally to trains (although this source of mortality may well be underestimated, as few people are in a position to record bodies on the railways). Records have been assessed on the likely reliability of the method used to make the record, and the likelihood of the record itself. For example, a record outside the previous known range of a species requires better than a blurred footprint to establish presence. Sight records of bats in flight have not been used. Many records have been extracted from published records and survey reports, and these usually do not have information on the nature of the original record. Some of the records came with no clear details of the nature of the record, but these have generally been accepted for common or easily identified species.

The major categories of the nature of the record are listed in Table 1.

Table 1. Number of records in the 12 largest categories of the nature of the record

Nature of record	Number of records
Sight	33 156 (29.0%)
Literature	16 322 (14.3%)
No details	14 159 (12.4%)
Molehills	9 204 (8.0%)
Trapping	9 089 (7.9%)
Road casualty	6 809 (5.9%)
Found dead	5 681 (5.0%)
Museum specimen	4 104 (3.6%)
Holes/burrows	2 833 (2.5%)
Faeces	2 602 (2.3%)
In bottle	1 676 (1.5%)
Killed	1 544 (1.3%)

The total number of records per species, and the number of distinct 10 km grid squares per species are shown in Table 2 (the two numbers preceding the species name are the rank numbers for the two columns).

It is little surprise that the mole was the most commonly recorded mammal, followed by rabbit and hedgehog. Moles leave easily observed signs of their presence – molehills, and rabbits and hedgehogs are easily observed, easily identified and common. The high positions of badger, grey squirrel, harvest mouse, red squirrel and otter are more surprising, but can be explained by the amount of survey work that has been done on these species, rather than by their abundance or ease of recording.

Table 2. Number of records and number of 10 km squares for each species

Rank	Species	No. of records	No. of squares	Rank	Species	No. of records	No. of squares
1 (2)	Mole	10808	2240	35(41)	Lesser horseshoe bat	841	268
2 (1)	Rabbit	8000	2294	36(36)	Dormouse	796	398
3 (3)	Hedgehog	6772	2015	37(37)	Natterer's bat	724	379
4 (4)	Badger	5484	1851	38(34)	Wild cat	693	406
5 (12)	Grey squirrel	5483	1476	39(38)	Daubenton's bat	662	327
6 (5)	Fox	5032	1776	40(35)	Common seal	560	403
7 (9)	Red squirrel	4841	1579	41(40)	Yellow-necked mouse	487	277
8 (13)	Pipistrelle	4356	1465	42(39)	Whiskered/Brandt's bat	456	290
9 (6)	Otter	4297	1775	43(48)	Greater horseshoe bat	415	146
10(7)	Brown hare	4125	1638	44(49)	Black rat	401	146
11(10)	Weasel	3640	1531	45(42)	Noctule	387	258
12(8)	Stoat	3515	1590	46(45)	Feral goat	340	172
13(11)	Common shrew	3394	1501	47(44)	Feral ferret	292	220
14(19)	Water vole	3007	1139	48(47)	Serotine	250	152
15(15)	Brown rat	2946	1426	49(50)	Whiskered bat	202	121
16(16)	Field vole	2737	1387	50(46)	Sika deer	198	155
17(14)	Wood mouse	2635	1427	51(51)	Barbastelle	140	93
18(17)	Roe deer	2599	1242	52(52)	Muskrat	124	86
19(21)	Mink	2468	1052	53(56)	Bechstein's bat	91	26
20(18)	Bank vole	2246	1152	54(54)	Brandt's bat	89	51
21(22)	Long-eared bat	2013	947	55(53)	Leisler's bat	88	58
22(20)	Pygmy shrew	1849	1067	56(59)	Orkney and Guernsey field vole	78	20
23(43)	Coypu	1668	227	57(55)	Chinese water deer	52	37
24(23)	House mouse	1463	919	58(60)	Fat dormouse	46	10
25(24)	Red deer	1392	801	59(57)	Grey long-eared bat	37	22
26(33)	Polecat	1385	409	60(58)	Red-necked wallaby	36	21
27(31)	Muntjac	1352	421	61(63)	Lesser white-toothed shrew	14	4
28(26)	Harvest mouse	1341	763	62(62)	Mouse-eared bat	14	6
29(25)	Water shrew	1228	771	63(64)	French shrew	8	3
30(27)	Fallow deer	992	576	64(61)	Parti-coloured bat	6	6
31(30)	Pine marten	920	454	65(65)	Greater white-toothed shrew	5	2
32(32)	Mountain hare	919	412				
33(28)	Grey seal	884	575				
34(29)	Brown long-eared bat	860	469				

There is a small group of mammals for which the ratio between the number of records and the number of squares for each species is particularly high. These species are listed in Table 3.

Table 3. Species with a large number of records compared with the number of squares from which they are recorded

Mole
Polecat
Muntjac
Lesser horseshoe bat
Greater horseshoe bat
Black rat
Bechstein's bat
Orkney and Guernsey field vole
Fat dormouse
Lesser white-toothed shrew

The mole is a widespread species which is particularly easy to record. Polecat, muntjac, lesser horseshoe bat, black rat and Bechstein's bat are species of restricted distribution which have been the subject of special surveys. The greater horseshoe bat has been studied in some detail, although there has been no special survey.

The other species in Table 3 are very restricted in their distribution.

Just over 115 000 records are now included in the data base. The majority of these (105 000, 91%) were collected between 1959 and 1988. Only 1400 records are dated from 1989–91, as no major effort has been made to gather in records made very recently.

The recorders

At least 1240 people have contributed records to the surveys in some way, but this figure does not include all those who have contributed through a third party, such as a county recorder, or those who have sent specimens to museums or to special surveys. The true number of contributors is therefore much higher. Recorders who have sent in over 1000 records are listed in Table 4.

The average number of records per recorder is 92.

Eighteen recorders contributed records from over 400 different 10 km squares and these are listed in Table 5. (Some have been extracted from published survey reports.)

The average number of squares covered is 28 per recorder.

Table 4. Recorders who have sent in over 1000 records

No. of records	Recorder
4041	P W Richardson, County Recorder for Northamptonshire
3355	Dr J A Gibson, Recorder for the Clyde Faunal Area
3118	Yorkshire Naturalists Union
2906	Dr A M Tittensor (including Welsh squirrel survey)
2593	W G Teagle
2491	NCC bat records
1926	Dr D W Yalden
1706	Dr H G Lloyd (squirrel survey 1971)
1631	Marion Browne, County Recorder for Wiltshire
1563	P Dunning (otter survey)
1423	Dr G B Corbet
1313	British Museum (Natural History)
1248	Dr P Morris
1218	E G Philp, County Recorder for Kent
1183	N D Redgate
1146	Forestry Commission
1133	Coypu Research Laboratory
1121	Norwich Castle Museum
1116	J and R Green (Scottish otter survey)
1115	National Game Census
1087	British Deer Society
1070	D I and N G Chapman
1009	G R Hill

Table 5. Recorders who have contributed records from over 400 10 km squares

No. of 10 km squares	Recorder
1358	H G Lloyd (1972 squirrel survey)
881	NCC bat records
860	J and R Green (Scottish otter survey)
789	M Shorten (1946 squirrel survey)
781	Dr A M Tittensor (including Welsh squirrel survey)
738	British Deer Society
730	Forestry Commission
592	British Museum (Natural History)
553	Mammal Society badger survey
524	Dr G B Corbet
486	Dr P Chanin (Mammal Society otter survey)
468	Dr P Morris
466	Dr S Harris
465	W G Teagle
432	Miss E J Lenton (English otter survey)
416	Dr D W Yalden
413	Sea Mammal Research Unit
412	V P W Lowe/Forestry Commission deer records

Irish mammals

The original Mammal Society and Deer Society surveys included Ireland, and most previously published maps have included Irish distribution. The Irish Biological Records Centre published distribution maps for mammals (and reptiles and amphibians) in 1974 and 1979. The majority of the Irish records gathered by the Mammal Society were passed to the Irish Records Centre. An Foras Forbartha, the department in which the Irish BRC was based, was closed in 1986, and it is believed that these records are now lodged with the National Parks and Wildlife Service. Since the closure of the Irish BRC, there has been no co-ordinated effort to record the general distribution of mammals in Ireland.

Vagrants

Northern bat (*Eptesicus nilssonii* (Keyserling & Blasius 1839))

Recorded once, at Betchworth in Surrey, in 1987, this bat is related to and resembles the serotine, and is common in eastern and central Europe. It appears to be increasing its range in Europe.

Nathusius's pipistrelle (*Pipistrellus nathusii* (Keyserling & Blasius 1839))

A western European species, this bat has been recorded several times in Britain, the Channel Islands and on North Sea oil rigs. It closely resembles the common pipistrelle and has probably been overlooked. The following mainland records are known:

Dorset, October 1969
Hertfordshire, August 1978
Essex, January 1985
Cornwall, January 1989
London, September 1989
Aberdeenshire, September 1989

Parti-coloured bat (*Vespertilio murinus* L. 1758)

This central and eastern European bat has been recorded five times in Britain and once on a North Sea oil rig. It is possible that some, or all, of these animals did not arrive unaided.

Plymouth, 1830+
off Great Yarmouth, 1834
Whalsay, Shetland, 1927
Mr Cap Oil Rig, 1965
Cambridge, 1985
Brighton, 1986

Hoary bat (*Lasiurus cinereus* (Palisot de Beauvois 1796))

This North American species has occurred once in Britain, on South Ronaldsay, Orkney, in September 1847. The origin of the specimen is uncertain, and it is possible it was transported on board a ship. The circumstances have recently been detailed in Hill and Yalden (1990).

Exotic escapes

Porcupines (*Hystrix* spp.)

Porcupines of several species have escaped from wildlife parks at various times, but on only one occasion do they seem to have established a breeding colony. In 1969 a pair of Himalayan porcupines (*Hystrix brachyura*) escaped from a wildlife park near Okehampton in Devon. They caused considerable damage in a forestry plantation by gnawing tree bark. Six were trapped in the following years, the last in 1979, and they are believed to have been eliminated from Britain (Smallshire & Davey 1989; Baker 1990).

Mongolian gerbils (*Meriones unguiculatus* (Milne-Edwards 1867))

A free-living population established itself for a while in the 1970s on the Isle of Wight, but did not last for many years (Sir Christopher Lever, pers. comm.). Other records are known from Yorkshire (Howes 1984).

Golden hamster (*Mesocricetus auratus* (Waterhouse 1839))

Golden hamsters are popular pets, and breed easily in captivity. Many must escape, or be set free each year, and from time to time wild breeding colonies are established, although usually these die out without any interference from man. One larger colony which apparently became established in Barnet, London, in the early 1980s was the subject of control measures, and some 130 animals were captured. However, this population had received extensive coverage in the press and on radio and television, and it seems likely that several additional animals were released into the area, distorting any estimate of the population size (Baker 1986).

Muskrat (*Ondatra zibethicus* (L. 1766))

Muskrats, like coypus, were brought to this country in the late 1920s to be farmed for their fur. Like the coypu, they escaped and began to breed in the wild. Feral populations established in Scotland, Shropshire, Sussex and Surrey (see map opposite). European experience had suggested that feral muskrat could be a serious threat to agriculture, and a determined campaign to eradicate them was begun in the early 1930s. By 1937 the species had been eliminated from Britain (Sheail 1988; Warwick 1940).

Red-necked wallaby (*Macropus rufogriseus* (Desmarest 1817))

Two populations of feral red-necked wallabies have been known in Britain. One, in the Peak District, started in 1940 and continues today, although there are very few animals remaining. The other, in Sussex, also started in 1940 but no records have been received since 1972. A free-living colony exists in the park at Whipsnade, and animals occasionally escape (see map on page 8). This species is popular in wildlife collections and other escapes have been noted from time to time.

Other species

Many species of mammals are kept in wildlife parks all over the country, and many escapes occur. Over 40 other species have been recorded as escaping in the last 20 years and, whilst many have been recaptured after as little as a day of freedom, some have been free for up to four years (wild boar, raccoon).

Muskrat

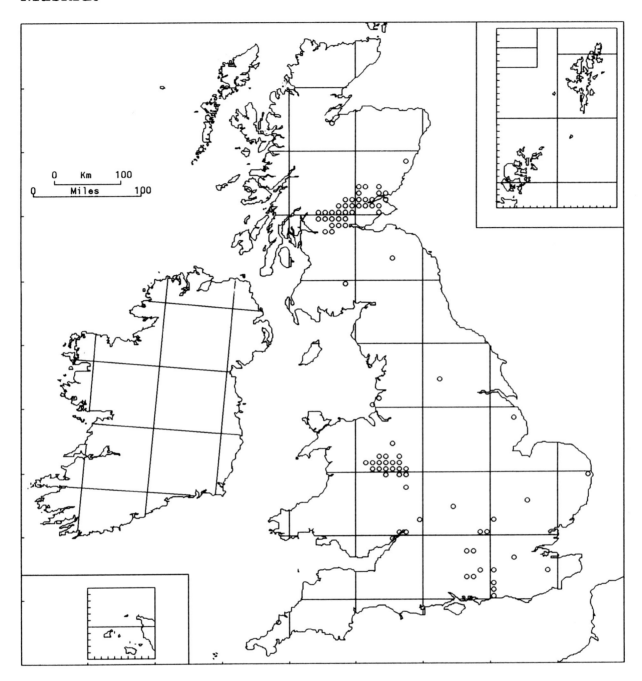

● 1960 onwards   (Great Britain 0, Channel Islands 0)

○ Up to 1959   (Great Britain 86, Channel Islands 0)

Red-necked wallaby

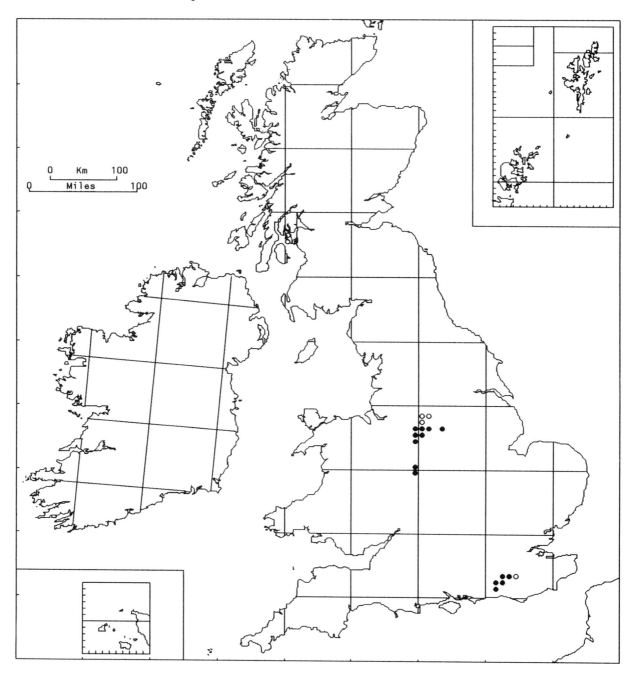

● 1960 onwards   (Great Britain-14, Channel Islands-0)

○ Up to 1959   (Great Britain-7, Channel Islands-0)

The possibility of other species establishing themselves clearly exists. The subject of escaping exotic animals is fully discussed by Baker (1990).

Records from islands

Distribution of taxa on small islands is difficult to represent clearly using 10 km squares of the National Grid, as several islands may occur in one square, or islands may occur in squares that also contain parts of the mainland. This makes it hard to tell whether some dots represent one island, or several, or mainland records.

For many mobile taxa, eg birds, this is not particularly critical, but with mammals the precise distribution on islands is of interest. There is no simple solution which overcomes this problem in maps of the scale presented here, and so the 10 km squares have been rigidly adhered to, and the positions of dots have not been adjusted as in earlier versions of the maps (Arnold 1978, 1984).

Instead, the Tables on pages 9–18 list the islands and the species that have been recorded on them. Some of these Tables may be incomplete; for example, some records have been extracted from other 10 km square maps, and it is not possible to assign island names to all of them.

Clearly, some mammals are much more mobile than others (bats, seals, otter) and their island distribution is of less interest, because there are fewer barriers to their dispersal, but they have been included for completeness.

Format

The species accounts are in the following format.

• **Species name and scientific name**

• **Handbook** Page numbers of the relevant section of *The handbook of British mammals* (Corbet & Harris 1991)

• **Status** Whether native or introduced. Abundance. Population trend, if data are available. The latter two categories are from Jefferies and Mitchell-Jones (1989). A brief comment on the species occurrence in Ireland

is given. Further information on the Irish distributions can be found in Corbet and Harris (1991) and in *The provisional distribution atlas of amphibians, reptiles and mammals in Ireland* (Ni Lamhna 1979)

• **Protection status** Whether the species is protected under British law, and by which Act

> WCA refers to the Wildlife and Countryside Act 1981 and later amendments. Schedule 5 of this Act lists species that are protected against killing, injuring or taking. Sites used by Schedule 5 species for shelter or protection are not allowed to be damaged, destroyed or have their access obstructed. Possession of, and trade in, live or dead Schedule 5 species is an offence. Schedule 6 outlaws certain methods of killing or trapping.

> BC refers to the Bern Convention (Convention on the Conservation of European Wildlife and Natural Habitats). The Convention requires that signatory States should:
>   i. protect the habitats of
>   ii. prohibit deliberate damage to important breeding and nesting sites of
>   iii. prohibit deliberate capture, killing, disturbance and trade in
> species listed in Appendix II.

> It also requires that signatory States should:
>   i. regulate the exploitation of
>   ii. ban certain means of capture or killing of
> species listed in Appendix III.

Deer are protected under several Acts and the legislation, which includes close seasons, is complex. Scottish legislation differs from that in England and Wales.

Badger legislation is also complex and the Badgers Act 1973 and amendments have been updated by the Badgers Act 1991 which gives some protection to the sett.

Seals are protected under the Conservation of Seals Act 1970.

These Acts are complex and summaries can be found in Cooper (1987), Harris and Jefferies (1991) or Prior (1983), for example, but, as with all legislation, the relevant Acts, Orders or Regulations should be consulted for a definitive view.

• **Description and recognition** Brief notes on the appearance of the species, and any particular problems with identification.

Further comments follow with some information on the records used to compile the maps. The number and percentage of each type of record is given; these percentages will not necessarily add up to 100 because a small number of miscellaneous record types accounting for less than 1% each are not included in the figures.

• **Map** A map is shown for most species, which includes all the records entered on the data base by March 1992. The information given in brackets represents the total number of squares in Great Britain and the Channel Islands for each date class. A small number of records which were sent to the Biological Records Centre after mid-1991 have not been entered.

Tables showing records from islands

Orkney Islands

	Eynhallow	Swona	Holm of Grimbister	Hoy	Shapinsay	Holm of Boray	Sweyn Holm	Rusk Holm	Pentland Skerries	Skelwick Skerry	Auskerry	Egilsay	Muckle Green Holm	Grass Holm	Holm of Scockness	Rousay	Cava	Stronsay	North Ronaldsay	South Ronaldsay	Mainland	Glims Holm	Wyre	Quanterness Skerry	Westray	Holm of Huip	Little Linga	Holm of Aikerness	Little Green Holm	Switha	Sanday	Flotta	Holm of Faray	Eday	Lamb Holm	Seal Skerry	Linga Holm	Wart Holm	Fara	Galt Skerry	Graemsay	Holms of Spurness	Claas Holm, Harray Loch	Inner Holm	Baa Holm, Harray Loch	Ling Holm, Harray Loch	Long Holm, Harray Loch	Papa Westray	Gairsay	Burray	Copinsay	Holm of Elsness	Skerry of Vinstay	Little Skerry	Sule Skerry	Faray
Hedgehog				•	•							•							•	•	•		•		•						•	•		•							•									•						
Water shrew				•																																																				
Pygmy shrew				•	•	•											•		•		•	•			•																•									•	•					
Noctule																			•	•											•																									
Pipistrelle																					•																																			
Brown hare																	•				•																																			
Mountain hare				•																																																				
Rabbit				•	•							•					•	•	•	•	•	•	•		•						•	•		•	•		•	•			•									•	•	•	•	•		
Wood mouse				•	•														•	•					•						•			•																	•					
Orkney field vole																	•	•			•				•						•												•		•	•	•									
House mouse	•	•	•	•								•						•	•	•	•				•						•	•									•								•	•	•					•
Brown rat				•	•	•						•						•	•		•		•								•	•									•			•						•						
Black rat																			•	•																																				
Otter	•			•	•							•					•	•	•	•	•	•	•								•	•		•							•									•	•					•
Grey seal	•	•		•		•	•	•	•		•	•	•						•	•	•		•		•	•	•				•	•	•		•		•	•					•							•	•			•	•	•
Common seal	•		•			•	•					•	•					•	•	•	•				•	•	•				•			•			•			•										•	•		•	•	•	

Shetland Islands

	Papa Stour	Langa	Whalsay	Mousa	Vaila	Green Holm, Burra	Muckle Roe	Papa Oxna	East Burra	Fair Isle	Bressay	Trondra	Mainland	Fetlar	Oxna	West Burra	Foula	Noss	Cunning Holm	Unst	Out Skerries	Linga	Urie Lingey	Yell	Vementry	Cheynies	Hascosay	Ve Skerries	Ladys Holm	Colsay	South Havra	Hildasay	Papa Little	Lamba	Gruney	Uyea, mainland	Bigga	Fish Holm	Little Holm	Muckle Holm	Brother Isle	Muckle Fladdicap	Linna Holm	East Linga	Crif Skerry	Isbister Holm	Moea	Nacka Skerry	Nista	Haaf Gruney	Gloup Holm	Uyea, Unst	North Holms	South Holms	Muckle Flugga
Hedgehog		●					●		●		●	●	●	●	●	●				●				●	●																														
Leisler's bat													●																																										
Pipistrelle													●																																										
Parti-coloured bat		●																																																					
Mountain hare				●																																																			
Rabbit	●	●	●			●	●	●	●		●	●	●	●	●	●	●			●	●	●		●	●	●															●														
Wood mouse										●			●	●		●								●																															
House mouse	●									●			●	●			●				●																																		
Brown rat													●							●	●																																		
Black rat		●											●																																										
Otter	●		●	●		●					●	●	●	●	●		●	●	●	●	●	●		●	●	●																													
Stoat							●						●																																				●						
Grey seal	●		●	●		●		●			●	●			●				●	●	●			●				●	●	●						●	●															●	●	●	
Common seal	●		●	●	●		●	●	●	●	●	●	●	●	●	●	●			●	●	●	●		●	●				●	●	●	●			●	●	●	●	●	●	●	●	●	●	●	●	●	●		●	●	●	●	●

Inner Hebrides

	Seil	Eigg	Muck	Outram	Tiree	Soa	Skye	Iona	Staffin	Shuna	Longa	Small Isles, Jura	Coll	Lismore	Scarba	Jura	Luing	Oronsay	Scalpay	Colonsay	Eilean Carmhna	Rona, Skye	Ulva	Soay, Skye	Eilean Creagach	Texa	Treshnish Isles	Rhum	Socuth Ascrib	Canna	Carna	Sandaig	Tanera Beg	Raasay	Mull	Gunna	Cara	Islay	Pabay	Little Colonsay	Gigha	Dubh Artach
Hedgehog							●	●					●											●											●			●				
Water shrew							●			●																									●	●		●	●			
Common shrew	●						●	●	●				●	●	●	●				●		●	●	●											●	●		●				●
Pygmy shrew	●	●	●				●	●					●	●	●	●			●	●			●				●	●							●	●		●	●			●
Mole	●						●																												●							
Pipistrelle							●							●										●											●			●				
Long-eared bat																																			●			●				
Brown hare				●	●		●						●			●																			●			●				●
Mountain hare							●									●																			●	●						
Rabbit	●						●	●	●				●			●						●	●	●		●									●	●		●	●	●	●	
Wood mouse	●	●					●	●	●				●	●	●	●		●						●						●					●	●		●			●	
Water vole																					●			●																		
Bank vole																				●				●											●	●						
Field vole	●	●					●		●				●	●	●	●			●				●												●			●				
House mouse			●				●	●					●		●					●						●												●			●	
Brown rat							●	●					●		●	●												●		●								●	●		●	
Otter	●		●	●	●		●		●	●			●	●		●	●	●	●			●	●					●		●		●		●	●	●		●	●	●		●
Pine marten							●																												●							
Stoat							●	●							●																				●			●				
Feral ferret																																			●			●				
Weasel							●								●																											
Fox							●	●								●																		●								
Grey seal			●		●	●	●		●				●	●		●		●	●			●		●			●	●	●						●			●	●		●	●
Common seal			●		●	●	●	●						●			●						●	●											●			●	●		●	●
Feral goat	●						●		●				●		●		●	●		●				●		●									●	●	●	●	●			
Roe deer							●								●																				●			●				
Red deer	●						●								●	●		●	●									●							●	●	●	●				
Sika deer							●																																			
Fallow deer														●																					●							

Outer Hebrides

Species	Lewis	Verran	Cighay	Benbecula	Eriskay	Vatersay	Soay	Harris	Shiant	St Kilda	North Uist	Dun	Baleshare	South Uist	Ceann Ear	Grimsay	Berneray	Stockay	Barra	Ronay	Sandray	Groay	Ceann Iar	Haskeir	Shillay	Flannan Isles	Casker
Hedgehog														●													
Common shrew	●																										
Pygmy shrew	●	●	●								●			●	●				●								
Long-eared bat											●																
Brown hare								●																			
Rabbit	●	●		●	●	●		●					●	●	●	●			●				●				
Wood mouse	●			●				●		●	●			●	●				●								
Field vole				●							●			●													
House mouse	●			●						●	●			●		●			●								
Brown rat	●	●	●								●			●		●			●								
Black rat	●			●					●																		
Otter	●			●					●	●	●					●	●	●	●	●	●						
Feral ferret														●													
Mink	●							●																			
Grey seal	●		●	●	●	●	●	●	●	●	●			●				●	●	●				●	●	●	●
Common seal	●								●		●			●				●	●	●				●			
Red deer	●			●					●		●			●						●							

Clyde Islands

	Lady Isle	Arran	Inchmarnock	Ailsa Craig	Little Cumbrae	Davaar	Pladda	Horse Island	Great Cumbrae	Sanda Group	Bute	Holy Island, Arran
Red-necked wallaby											●	
Hedgehog	●								●	●	●	
Water shrew	●						●		●		●	
Common shrew	●				●				●	●	●	
Pygmy shrew	●	●	●	●	●	●			●	●	●	●
Mole									●		●	
Natterer's bat	●											
Pipistrelle	●						●		●			
Long-eared bat	●								●			
Brown hare	●				●				●		●	
Mountain hare	●										●	
Rabbit	●	●	●	●	●	●		●	●	●	●	●
Wood mouse	●								●		●	
Water vole											●	
Bank vole	●										●	
Field vole	●								●		●	
House mouse	●	●						●	●	●	●	
Brown rat	●	●	●	●	●			●	●	●	●	
Black rat											●	
Red squirrel	●										●	
Otter	●	●	●	●	●	●		●	●	●	●	
Badger	●		●							●	●	
Stoat								●			●	
Feral ferret			●							●	●	
Weasel											●	
Polecat											●	
Mink	●											
Fox	●										●	
Grey seal	●	●	●	●	●	●	●	●	●	●	●	●
Common seal	●	●	●	●	●	●		●	●	●	●	●
Feral goat	●		●		●				●	●	●	
Roe deer	●									●	●	
Red deer		●			●					●	●	
Fallow deer					●						●	

15

Scilly Islands

	St Mary's	Burnt	Innisvouls	Gugh	Menawethan	Rat Island	St Agnes	Tresco	Seal Rock	Illiswilgig	Annet	Samson	Bryher	St Martin's
Lesser white-toothed shrew	●		●				●					●	●	●
Hedgehog	●													
Mole														●
Pipistrelle	●						●	●						
Rabbit		●		●			●	●			●			●
Wood mouse	●						●							
House mouse	●						●							
Brown rat	●						●							
Black rat						●								
Grey squirrel								●						
Otter	●													
Grey seal	●	●	●	●					●	●				
Fallow deer													●	

Channel Islands

	Alderney	Jersey	Herm	Sark	Guernsey	Lihou
Greater white-toothed shrew	●	●			●	
Lesser white-toothed shrew		●		●		
Hedgehog		●			●	●
French shrew		●				
Mole	●	●				
Pipistrelle	●	●			●	
Brown long-eared bat					●	
Grey long-eared bat		●				
Greater horseshoe bat		●			●	
Rabbit	●	●	●	●	●	●
Wood mouse	●	●	●	●	●	
Water vole					●	
Bank vole		●				
Orkney and Guernsey field vole					●	
House mouse	●	●		●	●	
Brown rat	●	●	●		●	●
Black rat	●	●		●	●	
Red squirrel		●				
Stoat		●			●	

Wight, Anglesey and Man

Species	Isle of Wight	Anglesey	Isle of Man
Hedgehog	●	●	●
Water shrew	●		
Common shrew	●	●	
Pygmy shrew	●	●	●
Mole	●	●	
Serotine	●		
Brandt's/Whiskered bat	●	●	
Bechstein's bat	●		
Daubenton's bat	●	●	
Whiskered bat	●		
Natterer's bat	●	●	●
Noctule	●	●	
Pipistrelle	●	●	●
Long-eared bat	●	●	●
Brown long-eared bat	●		●
Grey long-eared bat	●		
Greater horseshoe bat	●		
Lesser horseshoe bat		●	
Brown hare	●	●	●
Mountain hare			●
Rabbit	●	●	●
Wood mouse	●	●	●
Water vole	●	●	
Bank vole	●	●	
Field vole	●	●	●
House mouse	●	●	●
Dormouse	●		
Brown rat	●	●	●
Black rat		●	●
Grey squirrel		●	
Red squirrel	●	●	
Otter	●	●	

Species	Isle of Wight	Anglesey	Isle of Man
Badger	●	●	
Stoat	●	●	●
Feral ferret	●		●
Weasel	●	●	
Polecat		●	
Mink	●		
Fox	●	●	
Grey seal	●	●	●
Common seal		●	
Feral goat		●	●
Fallow deer		●	
Muntjac	●		

Miscellaneous A

	Lundy	Flat Holm	Steep Holm	Farne Islands	Lindisfarne	House Holm, Ullswater	Sharpitlaw Anna, River Tweed	Thorne Holme	Brownsea	Hayling Island	Handa	Walney	Hilbre	Ynys Dulas	Skomer	Caldey	Ramsey	Bardsey	Cardigan	Ynysoedd y Moelrhoniaid	St Margaret's, Caldey	Skokholm	Ynys Seiriol	Garland Stone	Grassholm	Ynys Feirig	Holy Island, Anglesey
Hedgehog												●															●
Water shrew					●																						
Common shrew						●			●	●				●		●	●										
Pygmy shrew	●								●	●				●													
Mole												●						●									●
Noctule																											●
Pipistrelle									●																		
Greater horseshoe bat															●												
Rabbit	●	●	●	●	●				●	●	●			●		●	●	●		●		●					●
Wood mouse									●	●	●	●		●													
Water vole						●				●		●															
Bank vole										●	●			●	●												
Harvest mouse									●																		
Field vole						●						●		●													●
House mouse		●										●										●					
Dormouse									●																		
Brown rat	●		●						●	●						●	●					●				●	●
Black rat	●																										
Red squirrel									●																		
Otter									●																		
Badger																											●
Stoat																											●
Weasel			●						●			●			●												●
Fox			●									●															●
Grey seal	●		●	●							●	●	●	●	●	●				●	●	●	●	●	●		●
Common seal			●																			●					
Feral goat	●																					●					
Roe deer								●																			
Sika deer	●																										
Muntjac		●																									

Miscellaneous B

Species	Ristol, Loch Broom	Whithorn	Eilean Subhainn, Loch Maree	Sgeirean Shallachain, Loch Linnhe	May	Inchlonaig, Loch Lomond	Clairinsh, Loch Lomond	Island I Vow, Loch Lomond	Inchcailloch, Loch Lomond	Inchfad, Loch Lomond	Torrinch, Loch Lomond	Creinch, Loch Lomond	Inveruglas, Loch Lomond	An Dun, Loch Tummel	Eilean Mor, Loch Sionescaig	Eilean Mor, Enard Bay	Eilean Mor, Loch Sunart	Calf of Man
Water shrew	●																	
Common shrew							●		●		●				●	●		
Pygmy shrew																		●
Mole	●								●		●				●			
Daubenton's bat									●									
Pipistrelle									●									
Long-eared bat																		●
Rabbit		●			●		●	●	●			●						●
Wood mouse	●														●			●
Bank vole									●		●							
Field vole									●					●				
House mouse					●													
Brown rat																		●
Grey squirrel									●		●							
Otter	●																	
Stoat									●									
Weasel										●								
Fox		●																
Grey seal			●	●												●	●	
Common seal					●													
Feral goat																		●
Roe deer									●									
Fallow deer						●			●		●							

Species accounts and maps

UK coverage of mammals

This map shows the coverage in terms of the number of records per 10 km square.

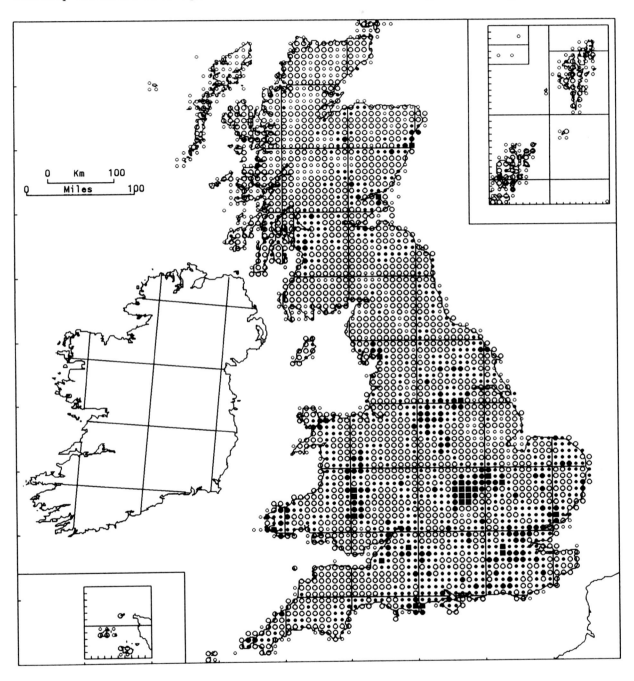

- ■ 201–327 records   (Great Britain 26, Channel Islands 0)

- ● 101–200 records   (Great Britain 159, Channel Islands 0)

- • 51–100 records   (Great Britain 571, Channel Islands 0)

- ○ 11–50 records   (Great Britain 1595, Channel Islands 5)

- ∘ 1–10 records   (Great Britain 474, Channel Islands 6)

Hedgehog

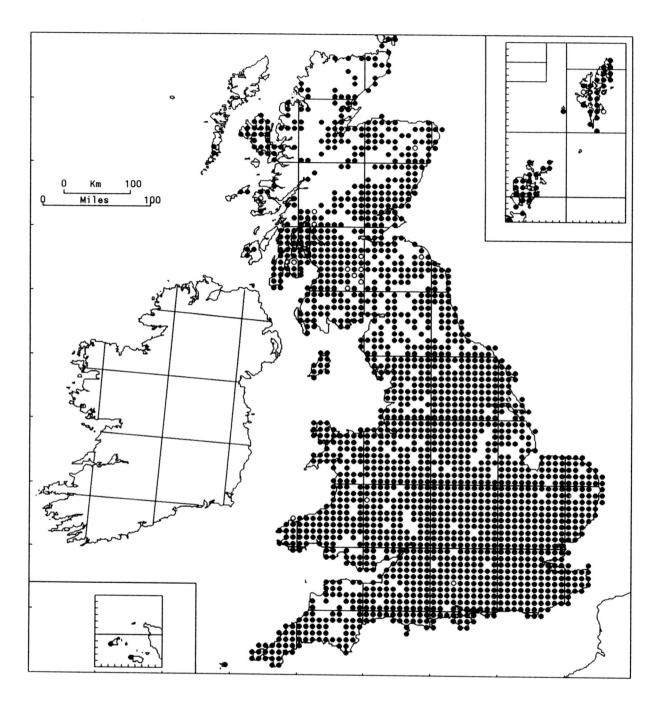

● 1960 onwards   (Great Britain 1991, Channel Islands 2)

○ Up to 1959   (Great Britain 22, Channel Islands 0)

Hedgehog (*Erinaceus europaeus* L. 1758)

Handbook 37-43.

Status Native. Common. Ireland – common and widespread.

Protection status WCA Schedule 6. BC Appendix III.

Description and recognition Its spines make the hedgehog instantly recognisable.

The hedgehog is likely to be found almost anywhere in mainland Britain where there is sufficient cover. It is most abundant at woodland edges or where hedges surround meadow land, but it has adapted well to suburban and urban areas and is frequently observed in gardens where it may be fed on the traditional bread and milk (although meaty cat food would be rather better for it). It is much less common in marshy areas and in mountainous regions that have no tree cover, although it may be found foraging at high altitudes and has been recorded at 1067 m (3435 ft) near the summit of Ben Lawers.

Out of a total of 6722 records, 5552 include details of the nature of the record:

Road casualty	3234	(58.2%)
Sight	1394	(25.1%)
Found dead	658	(11.9%)
Handled	90	(1.6%)
Museum specimen	66	(1.2%)

Of the 3234 road casualty records, 1688 have precise dates recorded. When plotted on a fortnightly basis, these dated records show several peaks, the first of which is in late-April to mid-May (Figure 1). Numbers fluctuate about this peak until late September when the number of road casualties declines. The spring peak in hedgehog mortality on the roads has been observed in other studies and has been attributed to an increased activity on emergence from hibernation (Brockie 1960).

Figure 1. Total number of road casualty records of hedgehogs for each fortnight

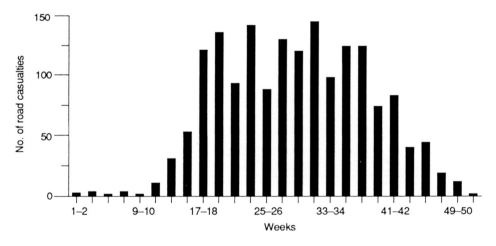

Small-island populations are all from introductions; in some instances, they are alleged to have caused problems by predating ground-nesting bird colonies.

Mole

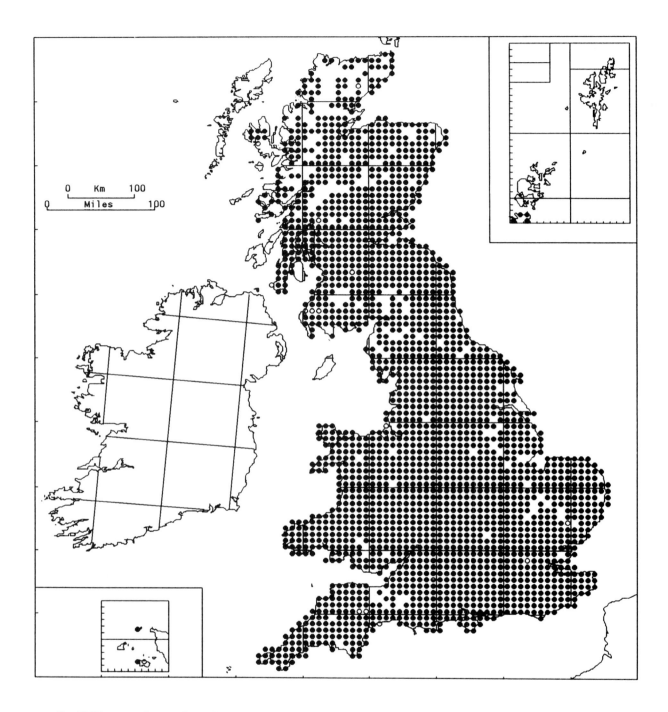

● 1960 onwards (Great Britain 2223, Channel Islands 2)

○ Up to 1959 (Great Britain 14, Channel Islands 1)

Mole (*Talpa europaea* L. 1758)

Handbook 44-49.

Status Native. Common.

Protection status

Description and recognition The velvety black fur and the feet adapted for digging make the mole unmistakable.

Moles are likely to be found anywhere on the mainland where there is sufficiently deep soil for them to dig their tunnels. Although they are originally animals of woodland, they can be found in open pasture, arable land, and even mountain moorland. The highest record is at 930 m (3050 ft) from Ben Lawers.

Out of a total of 10 808 records, 10 045 include details of the nature of the record:

Molehills	9204	(91.6%)
Found dead	250	(2.5%)
Museum specimen	194	(1.8%)
Sight	134	(1.3%)
Road casualty	68	(0.7%)

Molehills are most often recorded during the winter months (Figure 2), but this is more likely to be due to increased ease of visibility of molehills than greater activity of moles, although they probably produce rather fewer hills in dry summer weather when the ground becomes hard and dry and their invertebrate food retreats to lower levels in the soil.

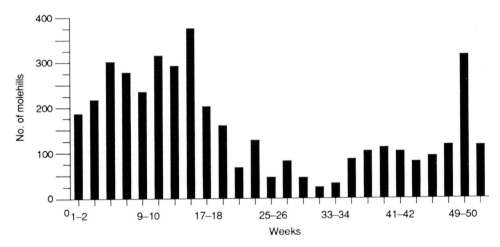

Figure 2. Total number of records of molehills for each fortnight

Common shrew

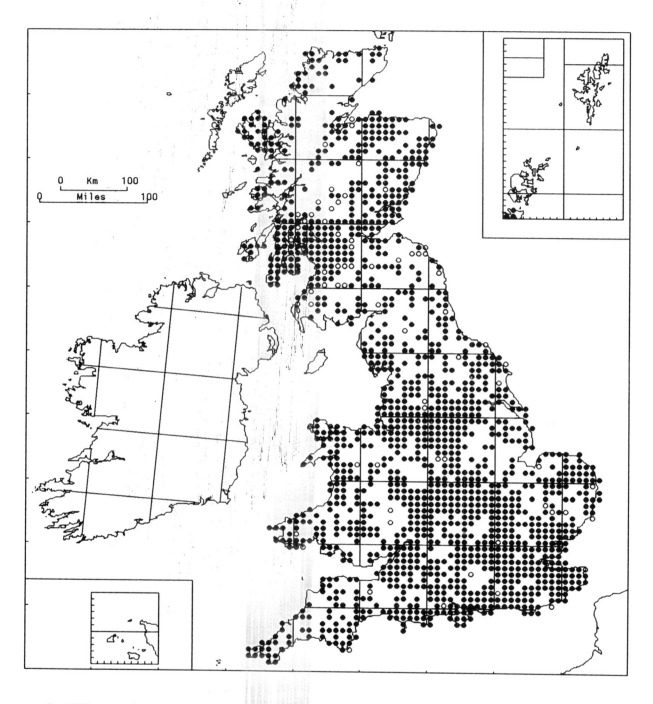

● 1960 onwards   (Great Britain 1429, Channel Islands 0)

○ Up to 1959   (Great Britain 72, Channel Islands 0)

Common shrew (*Sorex araneus* L. 1758)

Handbook 51-58.

Status Native. Abundant.

Protection status WCA
Schedule 6. BC Appendix
III.

Description and recognition The long snout distinguishes this small mammal as a shrew, the brown fur separates it from the water shrew, and the proportionally shorter tail distinguishes it from the pygmy shrew.

Common shrews are extremely widespread and can be found almost anywhere amongst vegetation and leaf litter. Although active throughout the day, periodically, they are infrequently seen. They have been recorded at 325 m (3000 ft) on Meall Greigh.

Out of a total of 3394 records, 2779 include details of the nature of the record:

In bottle	624	(22.5%)
Trapped	619	(22.3%)
Found dead	578	(20.8%)
Bird pellet	325	(11.7%)
Sight	232	(8.3%)
Museum specimen	213	(7.7%)

More dead common shrews were reported in mid- to late-summer (Figure 3), rather earlier than the October-November period described in other studies.

Figure 3. Total number of records of dead common shrews for each fortnight

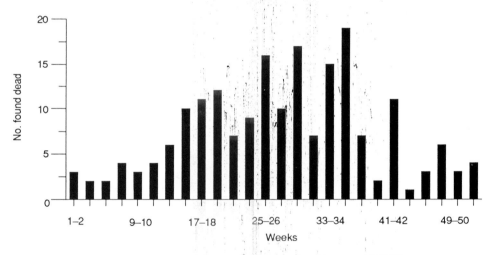

French shrew (Sorex coronatus Millet 1828)

Handbook 58-61.

Status Native - Jersey only.

Protection status

Description and recognition This species is indistinguishable on external characters from the common shrew.

It has long been known that there are chromosome races of the common shrew, and it has now been determined that the shrews on Jersey, although previously thought to be *Sorex araneus*, are in fact *Sorex coronatus*, the French (or Millet's) shrew (Ford & Hamerton 1970; Meylan & Hausser 1978). It is presumed to be similar to the common shrew in all other respects.

Pygmy shrew

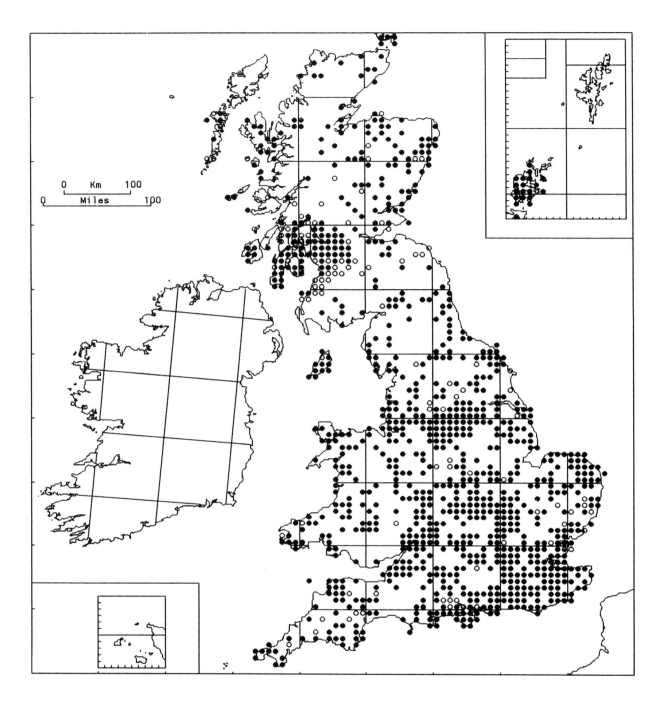

● 1960 onwards   (Great Britain 958, Channel Islands 0)

○ Up to 1959   (Great Britain 109, Channel Islands 0)

Pygmy shrew (*Sorex minutus* L. 1766)

Handbook 60-64.

Status Native. Common. Ireland - widespread.

Protection status WCA Schedule 6. BC Appendix III.

Description and recognition This small shrew is best distinguished from the common shrew by its proportionally longer tail (*c* 65% head and body length).

The pygmy shrew is also virtually ubiquitous on the mainland, but just as elusive as the common shrew. A pygmy shrew has been recorded from 1300 m (4400 ft) at the top of Ben Nevis, in a discarded bottle.

Out of a total of 1849 records, 1458 include details of the nature of the record:

Trapped	362	(24.8%)
Found dead	327	(22.4%)
Bird pellet	270	(18.5%)
In bottle	167	(11.5%)
Museum specimen	116	(6.3%)
Sight	105	(7.2%)
Cat kill	70	(4.8%)

Only 100 of the records of shrews found dead have full dates, and this is insufficient to reveal a clear seasonal pattern. For all types of records, the numbers peak in April and September (Figure 4).

Figure 4. Total number of records of pygmy shrews for each month

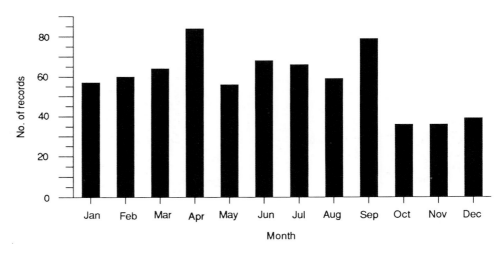

Water shrew

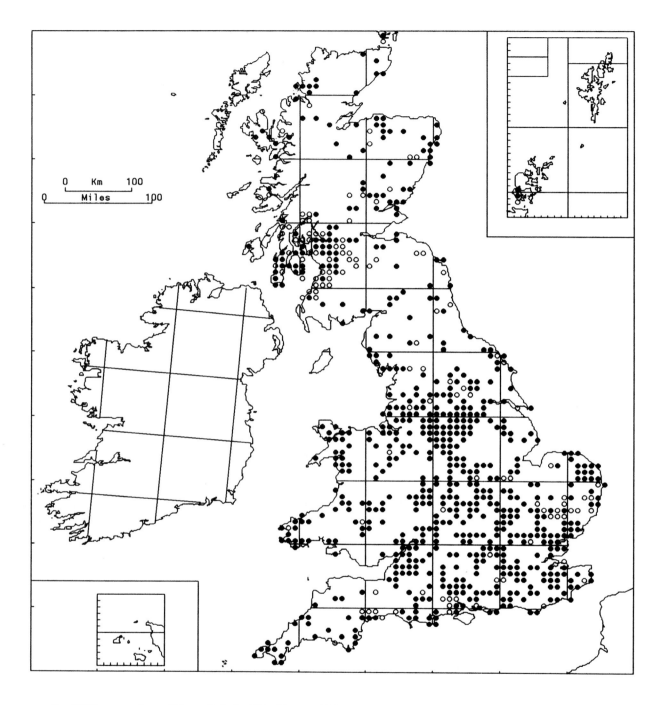

● 1960 onwards   (Great Britain 654, Channel Islands 0)

O Up to 1959   (Great Britain 117, Channel Islands 0)

Water shrew (*Neomys fodiens* (Pennant 1771))

Handbook 64-68.

Status Native. Common where it occurs.

Protection status WCA Schedule 6. BC Appendix III.

Description and recognition This is the most distinctive of the three widespread shrews, with its markedly contrasting dark (sometimes black) dorsal surface and pale (sometimes white) ventral surface.

It is usually found near streams and ponds, and is an excellent swimmer, as its English name suggests. However, it regularly occurs at large distances from water - reportedly up to 3 km in one instance (Southern unpublished, quoted by Jenkins 1977).

Out of a total of 1228 records, 882 include details of the nature of the record:

Sight	210	(23.8%)
Bird pellet	164	(18.6%)
Found dead	133	(15.1%)
Trapped	131	(14.9%)
In bottle	117	(13.3%)
Museum specimen	85	(9.6%)
Cat kill	32	(3.6%)

The numbers of records per month peak in April and July (Figure 5).

Figure 5. Total number of records of water shrews for each month

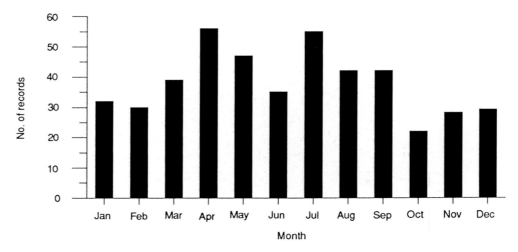

Greater and lesser white-toothed shrew

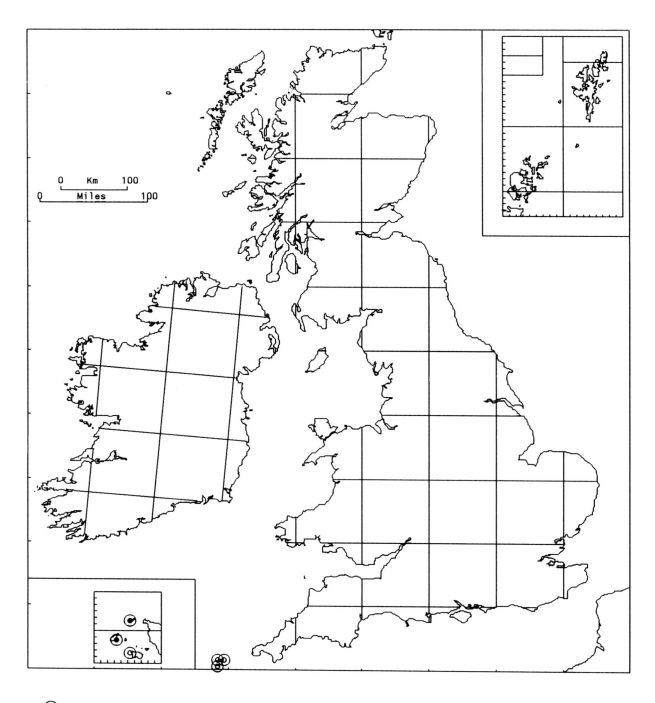

⊙ Greater white-toothed shrew   (Great Britain 0, Channel Islands 2)

◎ Lesser white-toothed shrew   (Great Britain 3, Channel Islands 1)

Lesser white-toothed shrew (*Crocidura suaveolens* (Pallas 1811))

Handbook 68-72.

Status Probably introduced to the Scilly Isles in the Iron Age or earlier. On some of the Scilly and Channel Isles.

Protection status

Description and recognition This is the only shrew on those islands where it is found, except for Jersey where the French shrew also occurs. It is distinguished from the French shrew by its unpigmented teeth and more prominent ears.

Greater white-toothed shrew (*Crocidura russula* (Hermann 1780))

Handbook 72-75.

Status Probably introduced. On some Channel Islands only.

Protection status

Description and recognition Again, this is the only shrew on those islands on which it occurs. It has unpigmented teeth, and larger ears than *Sorex* or *Neomys*.

Greater horseshoe bat

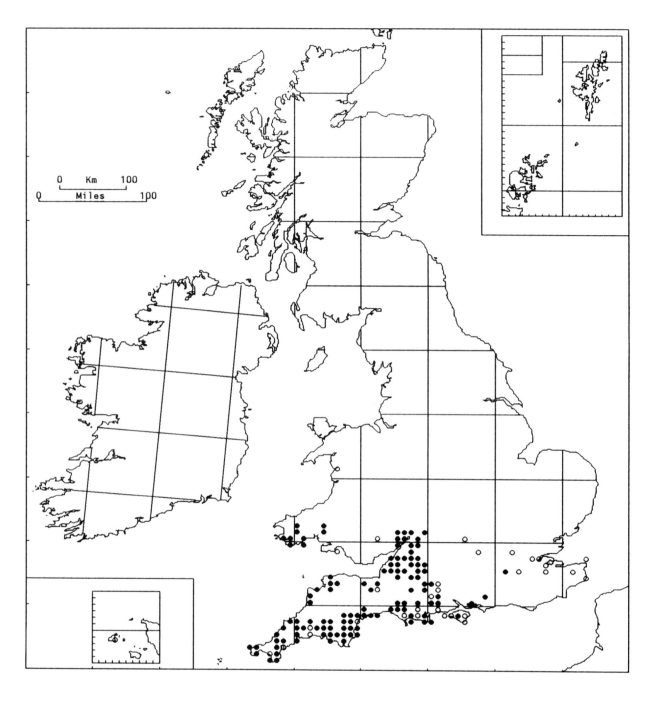

● 1960 onwards   (Great Britain 114, Channel Islands 0)

○ Up to 1959   (Great Britain 31, Channel Islands 1)

Greater horseshoe bat (*Rhinolophus ferrumequinum* (Schreber 1774))

Handbook 88-94.

Status Native.
Endangered. Declining.

Protection status WCA
Schedule 5. BC Appendix
II.

Description and recognition The greater horseshoe bat should be easily recognised by the horseshoe-shaped nose-leaf. The only other British species to have this nose-leaf is the lesser horseshoe bat, which is much smaller, with the forearm less than 45 mm.

Unlike most other bats, the horseshoe bats do not hide in crevices, but hang free from the roofs of caves, mines or buildings, and hence are usually easily observed. Unlike most other bats, they prefer free flight access to their roosting sites.

Out of a total of 415 records, 318 include details of the nature of the record:

Close sight	146	(45.9%)
In hand	128	(40.3%)
Museum specimen	22	(6.9%)
Found dead	21	(6.6%)

Now confined to south-west England and south Wales, this species was formerly much more common and widespread. Of 58 nursery sites identified from a variety of sources, only 14 are currently used (Stebbings & Arnold 1990), and numbers of bats at several of these have declined considerably in the last century. Although formerly roosting in caves in both winter and summer, this species now depends on buildings during the summer as few cave sites provide sufficiently high temperatures for successful breeding. When populations were higher, bats could generate higher temperatures by clustering together, but numbers have declined to such an extent that this is no longer possible. Only 42% of records are for the summer months (Figure 6).

Figure 6. Total number of records of greater horseshoe bats for each month

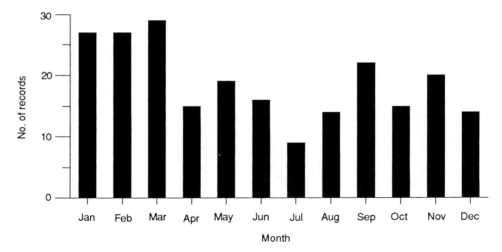

Lesser horseshoe bat

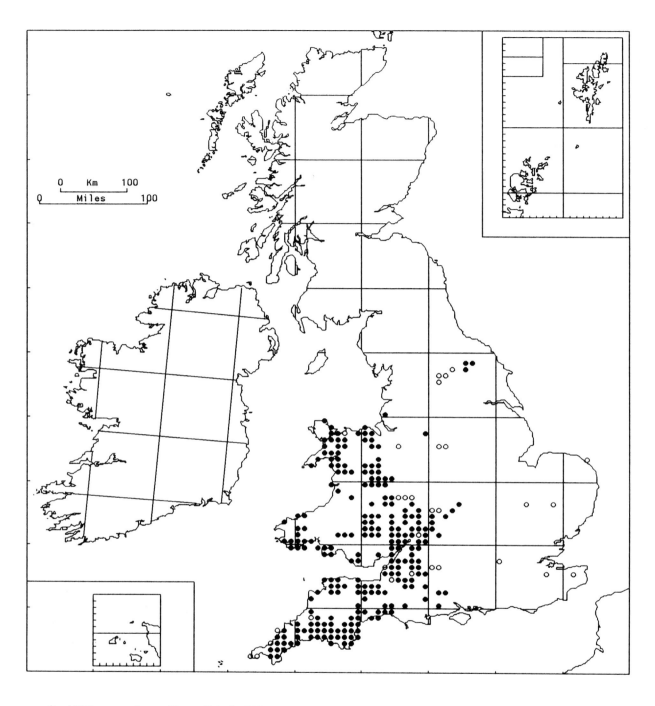

● 1960 onwards   (Great Britain 238, Channel Islands 0)

○ Up to 1959   (Great Britain 30, Channel Islands 0)

Lesser horseshoe bat (*Rhinolophus hipposideros* (Bechstein 1880))

Handbook 95-97.

Status Native. Endangered. Declining. Ireland - confined to the south-west.

Protection status WCA Schedule 5. BC Appendix II.

Description and recognition The nose-leaf and the small size distinguish this species.

Like the greater horseshoe bat, this species depends to a large extent on buildings for breeding, and is equally obvious in its roosting sites.

Out of a total of 841 records, 494 include details of the nature of the record:

Close sight	295	(59.7%)
In hand	140	(28.3%)
Museum specimen	41	(8.3%)
Found dead	11	(2.2%)
Road casualty	5	(1.0%)

Lesser horseshoe bats also prefer to have free flight access to their roosting sites, and so are usually found in large, old buildings. Modern restoration of such buildings can exclude colonies.

Although some colonies are known to have declined or even disappeared, the lesser horseshoe is still widely distributed in Wales and south-west England. The recent records in Yorkshire are all hibernation site records dating from the early 1980s, and its current status in this area is unknown.

Nearly 46% of records are for the summer months (Figure 7).

Figure 7. Total number of records of lesser horseshoe bats for each month

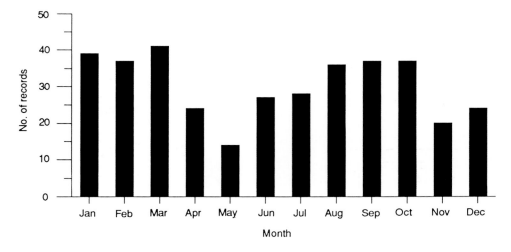

37

Whiskered/Brandt's bats

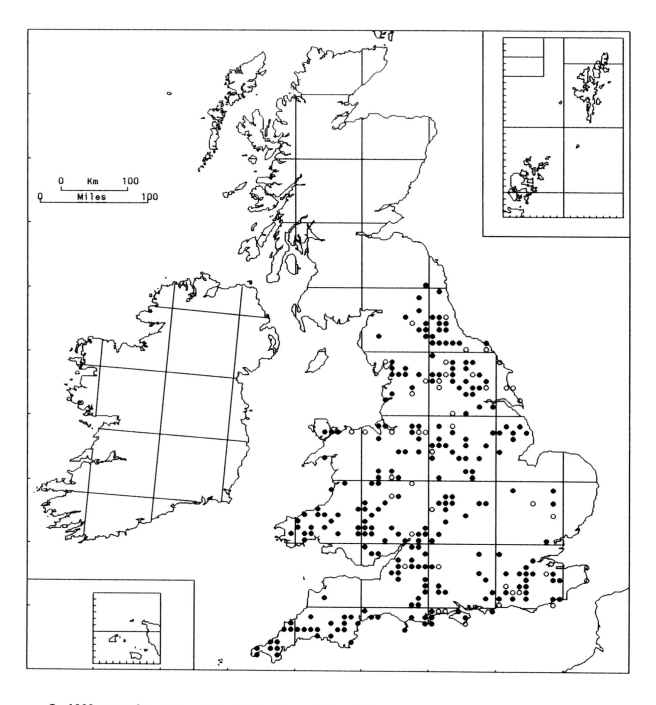

● 1960 onwards   (Great Britain 245, Channel Islands 0)

○ Up to 1959   (Great Britain 45, Channel Islands 0)

Whiskered/Brandt's bats

Until 1970 whiskered and Brandt's bats were regarded as one species, the whiskered bat. Since the two have been separated, a number of older museum specimens have been re-examined and some specimens have been re-identified as Brandt's bats. They are extremely difficult to tell apart and many records cannot be assigned accurately to one or other species; hence, the two species are mapped as one where the determination has not been made.

Out of a total of 456 records, 265 include details of the nature of the record:

In hand	129	(48.7%)
Close sight	57	(21.5%)
Found dead	38	(14.3%)
Museum specimen	29	(10.9%)

Whiskered bat

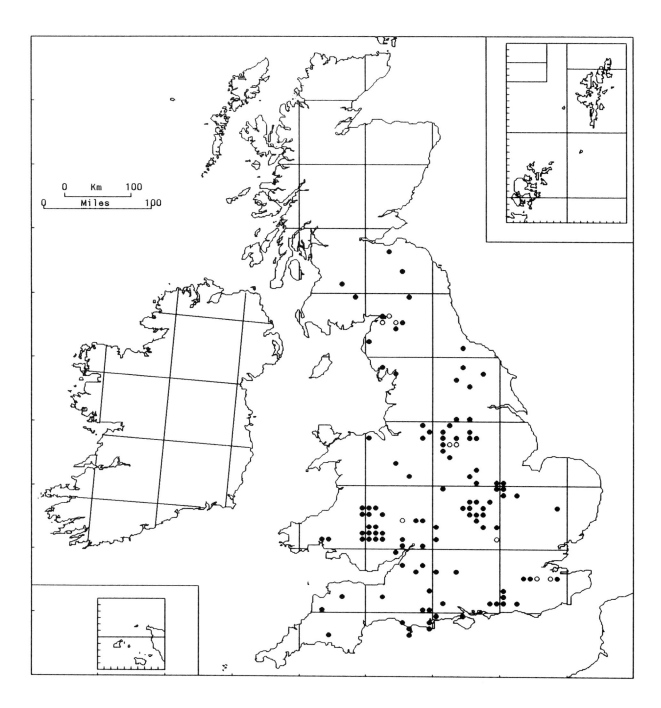

● 1960 onwards   (Great Britain 112, Channel Islands 0)

○ Up to 1959   (Great Britain 9, Channel Islands 0)

Whiskered bat (*Myotis mystacinus* (Kuhl 1819))

Handbook 99-101.

Status Native. Vulnerable. Declining. Ireland - widespread.

Protection status WCA Schedule 5. BC Appendix II.

Description and recognition A small *Myotis* bat (no post-calcarial lobe, more or less pointed tragus), it has dark skin and small ears, and is very difficult to separate from Brandt's bat. Careful examination of the shape of the ear and tragus, and possibly examination of the teeth, is needed.

Out of a total of 202 records, 194 include details of the nature of the record:

In hand	82	(42.3%)
Museum specimen	70	(36.1%)
Found dead	23	(11.9%)
Cat kill	10	5.2%)
Close sight	6	(3.1%)

As well as being found in caves in winter, it is quite frequently found in houses in the summer. Sixty per cent of records are for the summer months (Figure 8).

Figure 8. Total number of records of whiskered bats for each month

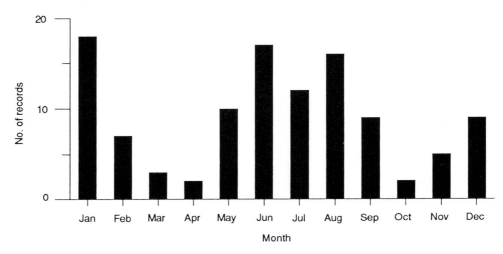

Brandt's bat

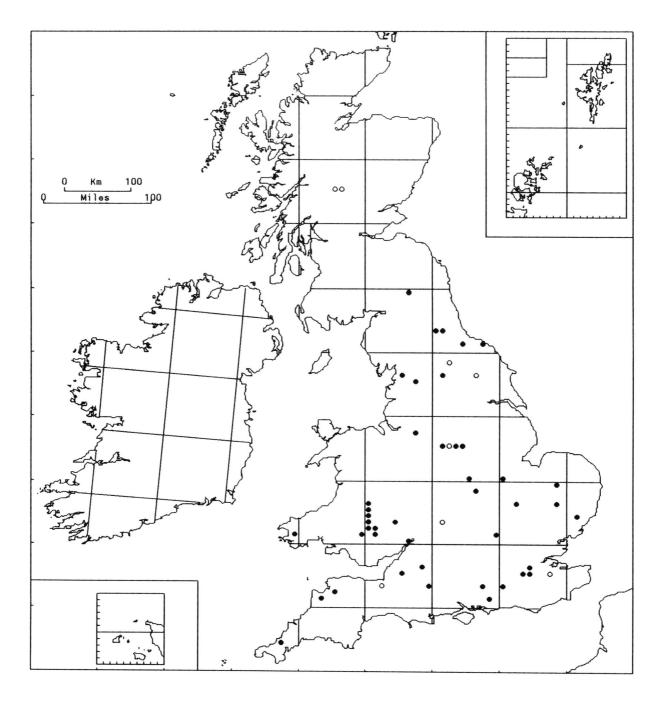

● 1960 onwards   (Great Britain 43, Channel Islands 0)

○ Up to 1959   (Great Britain 8, Channel Islands 0)

Brandt's bat (*Myotis brandtii* (Eversmann 1845))

Handbook 101-102.

Status Native. Vulnerable. Declining.

Protection status WCA Schedule 5. BC Appendix II.

Description and recognition A small *Myotis* bat (no post-calcarial lobe, more or less pointed tragus), it has slightly redder upper fur than the whiskered bat.

Only recently identified as a separate species, there are few records for this bat. Almost nothing is known about its biology, although it is assumed to be similar in many respects to the whiskered bat.

Out of a total of 89 records, 88 include details of the nature of the record:

In hand	54	(61.4%)
Museum specimen	26	(29.5%)
Found dead	4	(4.5%)
Close sight	1	(1.1%)
Road casualty	1	(1.1%)
Cat kill	1	(1.1%)
Dog kill	1	(1.1%)

Found in underground sites during hibernation as well as in buildings in the summer months. Only 40 records have the month given and they show no clear pattern.

Natterer's bat

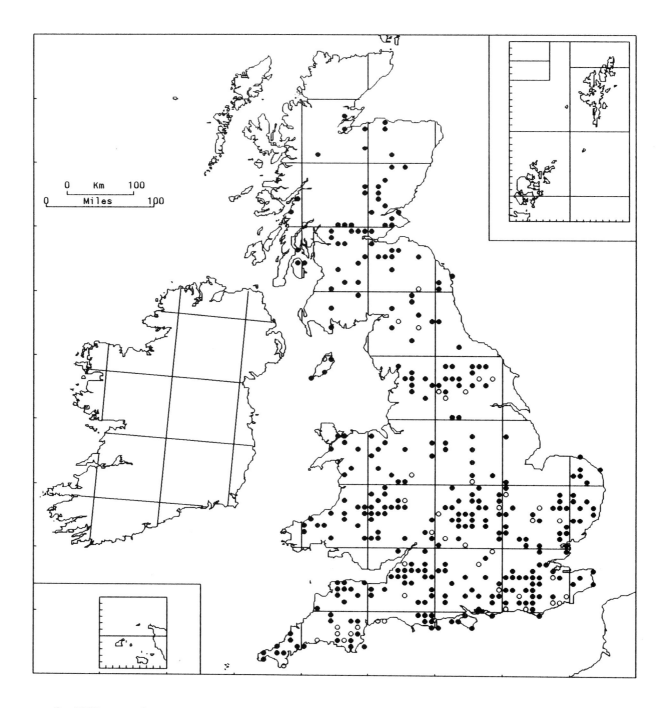

● 1960 onwards   (Great Britain 334, Channel Islands 0)

○ Up to 1959   (Great Britain 45, Channel Islands 0)

Natterer's bat (*Myotis nattereri* (Kuhl 1818))

Handbook 102-105.

Status Native. Vulnerable. Declining. Ireland - widespread.

Protection status WCA Schedule 5. BC Appendix II.

Description and recognition The most distinctive feature of this medium-sized *Myotis* bat is the fringe of short, stiff bristles along the edge of the tail membrane from the tail to the end of the calcar. It has longish (*c* 16 mm) ears and a slender tragus.

This is mainly a bat of woodland edge and parkland, but it is also found in more densely wooded areas such as conifer plantations.

Out of a total of 724 records, 573 include details of the nature of the record:

Close sight	240	(41.9%)
In hand	171	(29.8%)
Museum specimen	65	(11.3%)
Found dead	57	(9.9%)
Bird pellet	14	(2.4%)
Cat caught	10	(1.7%)
Road casualty	10	(1.7%)

This species hibernates in cave-like sites and in the summer is found in buildings. Hibernating bats account for a large number of the records, but there is also a peak of records in July and August which are mainly from roosts in houses (Figure 9).

Figure 9. Total number of records of Natterer's bats for each month

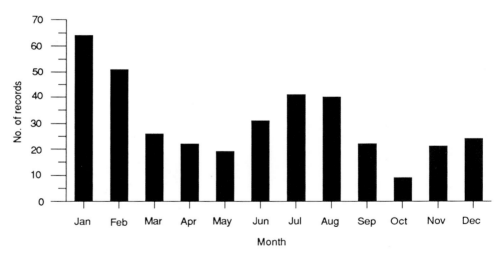

Bechstein's bat

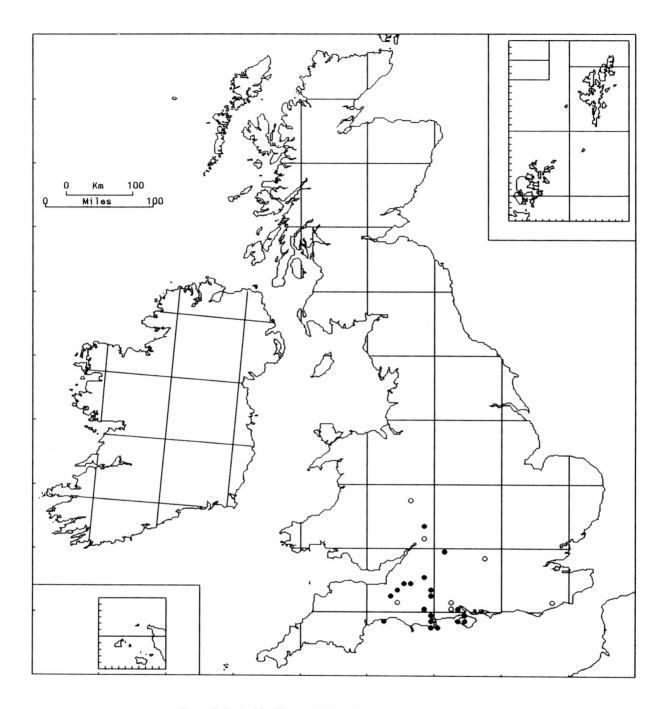

● 1960 onwards   (Great Britain 19, Channel Islands 0)

○ Up to 1959   (Great Britain 7, Channel Islands 0)

Bechstein's bat (*Myotis bechsteinii* (Kuhl 1818))

Handbook 105-107.

Status Native. Rare.

Protection status WCA
Schedule 5. BC Appendix
II.

Description and recognition The large ears, which do not meet at the base as do those of the long-eared bats, distinguish this species.

Bechstein's is a woodland species; on the continent it roosts in tree holes and buildings in the summer. It hibernates in caves and cave-like sites. No breeding colonies are known in Britain, all the summer records being of single individuals. It has never been a common species in Britain in recent times, although examination of bones from cave deposits some 3000-4000 years old suggest that it was more widespread and numerous at that time. It is now confined to a few counties in the south-west of England. Of the 87 dated records, 53% are from the winter months. All records are detailed by Stebbings (1989).

Mouse-eared bat

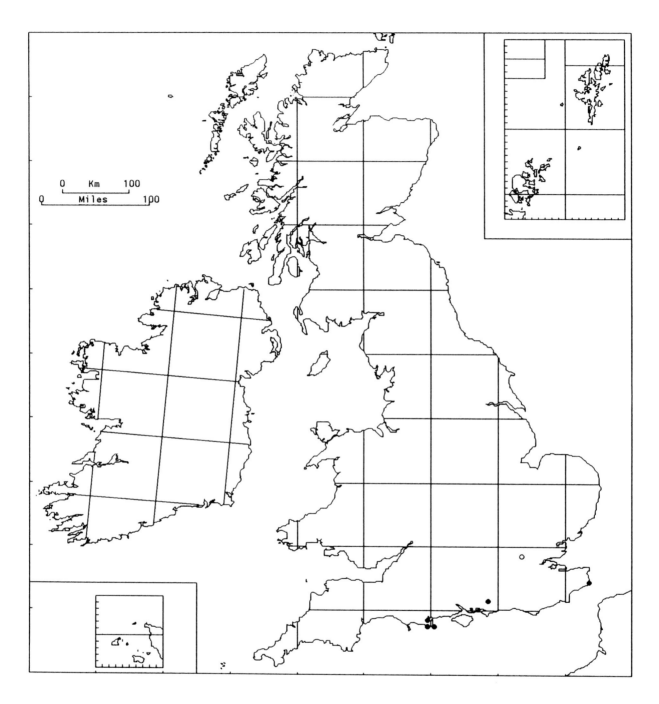

● 1960 onwards   (Great Britain 5, Channel Islands 0)

○ Up to 1959   (Great Britain 1, Channel Islands 0)

Mouse-eared bat (*Myotis myotis* (Borkhausen 1797))

Handbook 107-108.

Status Native. Probably extinct.

Protection status WCA Schedule 5. BC Appendix II.

Description and recognition This largest British species has a forearm over 57 mm.

It is now believed to be extinct in Britain, none having been seen since January 1990, and having been represented by a single male for several years prior to that. Only two populations have been known; the Dorset colony was known only from hibernation sites and was extinct by 1980, possibly because of too much disturbance. The Sussex colony was rather larger (up to 30) but no adult females were found after 1974, and it was concluded that the nursery cluster had been destroyed. Most bats were found in hibernation sites but two were killed in summer 1978 when a hollow tree was felled.

The pre-1960 record from TQ38 dates from before 1850 and refers to a bat found in the grounds of the British Museum. The Kent record (TR34) is of a single animal found hibernating in the winter of 1985.

Daubenton's bat

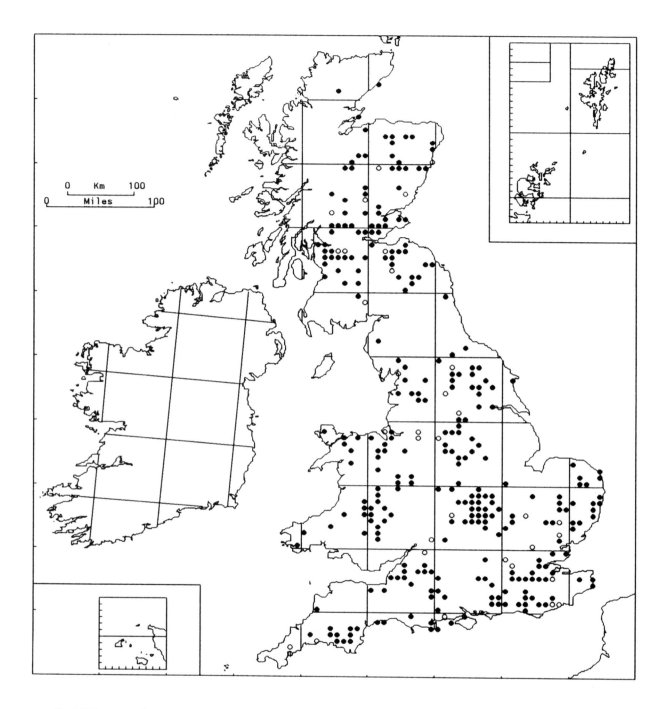

● 1960 onwards   (Great Britain 293, Channel Islands 0)

○ Up to 1959   (Great Britain 34, Channel Islands 0)

Daubenton's bat (*Myotis daubentoni* (Kuhl 1819))

Handbook 108-111.

Status Native. Vulnerable. Declining?   Ireland - Widespread.

Protection status WCA Schedule 5. BC Appendix II.

Description and recognition This is a small *Myotis* bat (no post-calcarial lobe and a more or less pointed tragus), with large feet (greater than half the length of the shin). It has even-textured, rather mole-like fur.

Out of a total of 662 records, 514 include details of the nature of the record:

In hand	231	(44.9%)
Close sight	194	(37.7%)
Museum specimen	48	(9.3%)
Found dead	32	(6.2%)
Road casualty	4	(0.8%)

Although often referred to as the water bat, Daubenton's is not the only species to be found near water, neither does it necessarily roost near water. It inhabits open wooded areas and is one of the species which hibernates in caves and other underground sites. Fifty-seven per cent of the dated records are from the winter months (Figure 10).

Figure 10. Total number of records of Daubenton's bats for each month

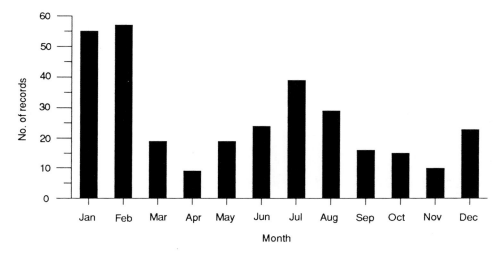

It is widely distributed throughout Britain and is certainly more common than the map shows, particularly in southern England.

Serotine

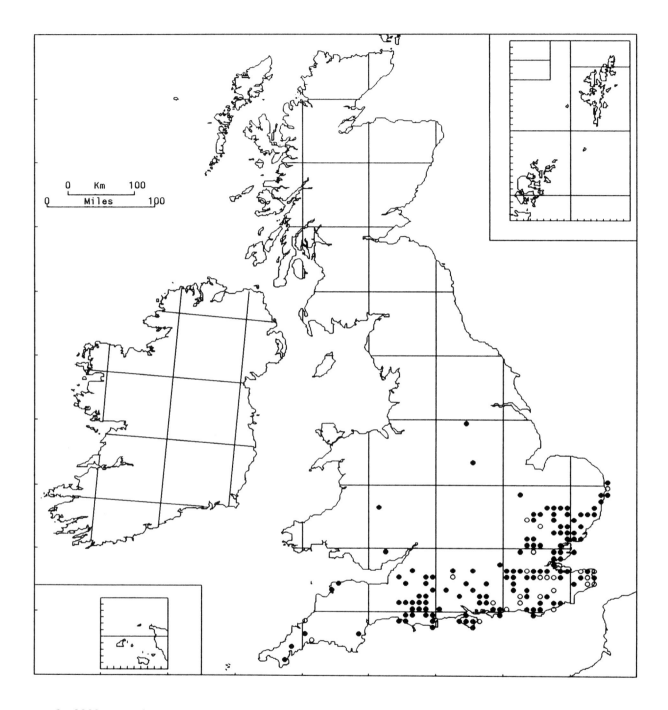

● 1960 onwards   (Great Britain 128, Channel Islands 0)

○ Up to 1959   (Great Britain 24, Channel Islands 0)

Serotine (*Eptesicus serotinus Schreber* 1774)

Handbook 112-116.

Status Native. Vulnerable. Declining.

Protection status WCA Schedule 5. BC Appendix II.

Description and recognition One of the largest British species, its size, the blunt, finger-shaped tragus and broad wings should distinguish it from the other large bats.

Although a species of open woodland and parkland, it is very strongly associated with buildings and almost never hibernates in caves in this country (although it does so in Europe). Consequently, there are few records from the winter months.

Out of a total of 250 records, 148 include details of the nature of the record:

In hand	85	(57.4%)
Museum specimen	29	(19.6%)
Close sight	22	(14.9%)
Found dead	15	(10.1%)

Of the 134 dated records, only 24 (18%) are from the period October-March when the animal is hibernating but 60 (45%) are from the peak months of July and August (Figure 11).

Figure 11. Total number of records of serotines for each month

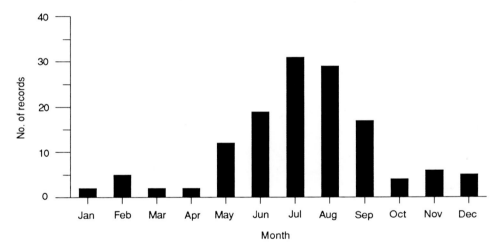

Most records are from the south-east, but there are a few recent records from the south-west and Wales and two more northerly records (Nottinghamshire and Yorkshire). There is no evidence that this demonstrates an increasing population.

Noctule

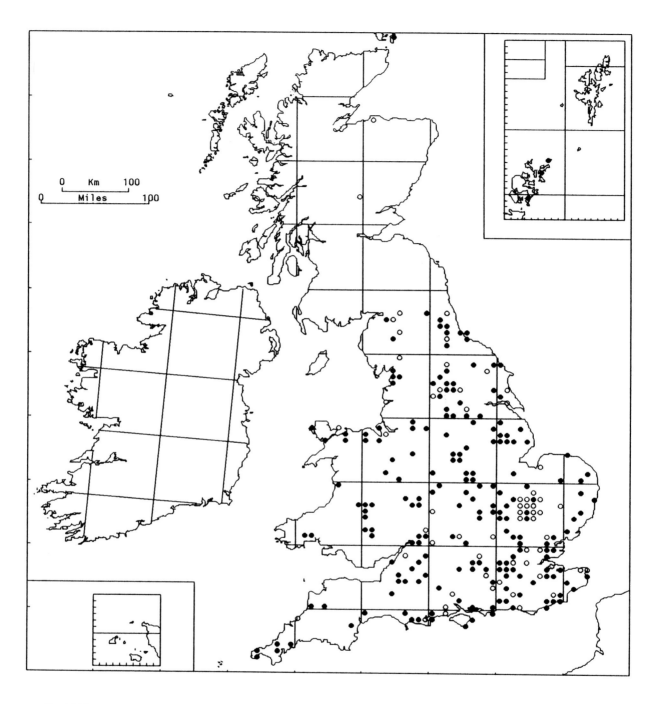

● 1960 onwards   (Great Britain 199, Channel Islands 0)

○ Up to 1959   (Great Britain 59, Channel Islands 0)

Noctule (*Nyctalus noctula* (Schreber 1774))

Handbook 117-121.

Status Native. Vulnerable. Declining.

Protection status WCA Schedule 5. BC Appendix II.

Description and recognition The only species that might be confused with the noctule is Leisler's bat. They both have rounded ears and a short, almost mushroom-shaped tragus. The noctule is larger with a forearm of over 47 mm, and has smooth, almost glossy, fur. The hairs are uniformly coloured from base to tip.

Out of a total of 387 records, 255 include details of the nature of the record:

In hand	117	(45.9%)
Museum specimen	78	(30.6%)
Found dead	36	(14.1%)
Close sight	9	(3.5%)
Road casualty	3	(1.2%)
Photograph	3	(1.2%)
Killed	3	(1.2%)

The noctule is a woodland species and rarely enters cave-like sites in Britain, so is only occasionally recorded in winter. It is sometimes found in hibernation when hollow trees are felled, usually to the detriment of the bats. Seventy-five per cent of the dated records are from the summer months (Figure 12).

Figure 12. Total numbers of records of noctules for each month

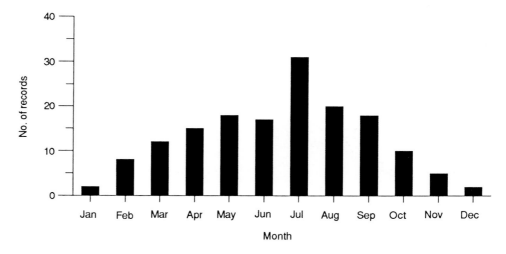

Colonies in hollow trees are sometimes extremely noisy and the bats can be heard from some distance away. It is widespread over most of England and Wales. The two pre-1960 Scottish records date from 1904 (NN94) and 1909 (NJ16). The Orkney records, in 1976, 1978 and 1988, are assumed to be vagrants. There are unconfirmed flight records from the Borders region in the 1980s.

Leisler's bat

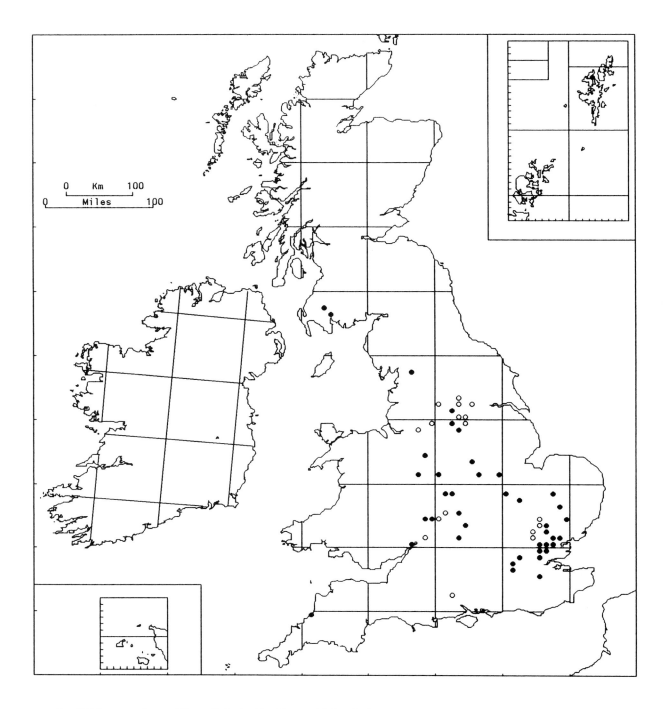

● 1960 onwards   (Great Britain 41, Channel Islands 0)

○ Up to 1959   (Great Britain 17, Channel Islands 0)

Leisler's bat (*Nyctalus leisleri* (Kuhl 1818))

Handbook 121-123.

Status Native. Rare and vulnerable. Ireland - widespread.

Protection status WCA Schedule 5. BC Appendix II.

Description and recognition This species is very similar to, but smaller than (forearm less than 47 mm), the more common noctule. The fur is more shaggy and the hairs are dark at the base.

Out of a total of 88 records, 62 include details of the nature of the record:

In hand	26	(41.9%)
Museum specimen	15	(24.2%)
Found dead	14	(22.6%)
Close sight	3	(4.8%)
Photograph	2	(3.2%)

Like the noctule, Leisler's is essentially a woodland species, and is rarely, if ever, found in cave-like sites in Britain. Some summer colonies are found in houses but bats are hardly ever found in hibernation. Only four of the 38 dated records are from the winter months (Figure 13).

Figure 13. Total number of records of Leisler's bats for each month

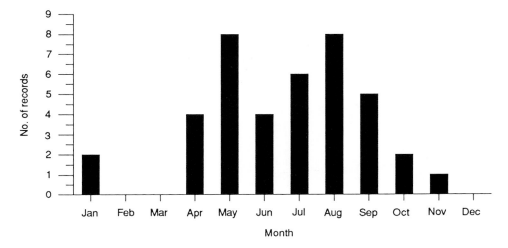

Two individuals have recently (1988 and 1991) been recorded from south-west Scotland. The Shetland record dates from 1968 and is assumed to be a vagrant.

Pipistrelle

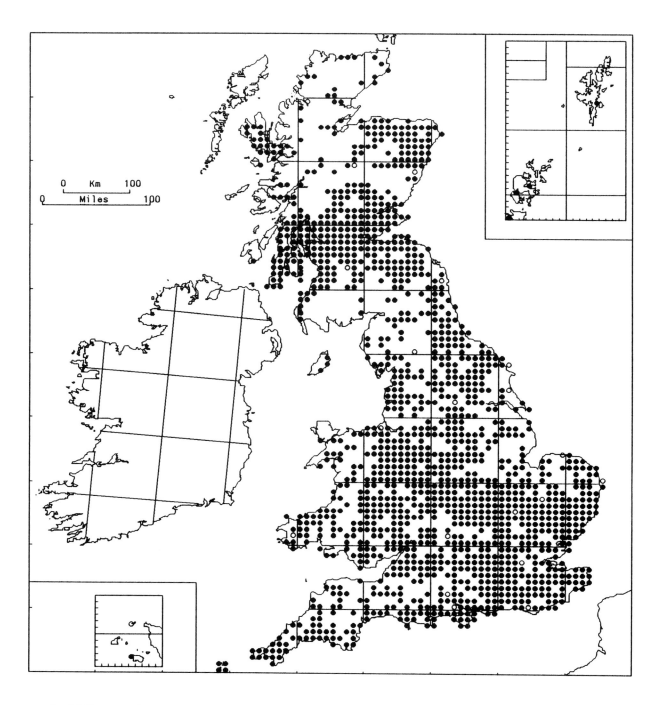

● 1960 onwards   (Great Britain 1441, Channel Islands 1)

○ Up to 1959   (Great Britain 22, Channel Islands 1)

Pipistrelle (*Pipistrellus pipistrellus* (Schreber 1774))

Handbook 124-128.

Status Native. Vulnerable. Declining. Ireland - widespread.

Protection status WCA Schedule 5. BC Appendix III.

Description and recognition The pipistrelle is the smallest British species, with a forearm of less than 35 mm. It has a blunt finger-like tragus and a post-calcarial lobe. It may be confused with other *Pipistrellus* species, but so far only *P. nathusii* has been found, and only on a very few occasions.

It is the commonest and most widespread bat in Britain, and, because it frequently roosts in modern houses in the summer, it is the bat which most often comes to the notice of members of the public.

Out of a total of 4356 records, 3037 include details of the nature of the record:

In hand	1345	(44.3%)
Found dead	617	(20.3%)
Close sight	606	(20.0%)
Museum specimen	240	(7.9%)
Cat kill	58	(1.9%)
Road casualty	35	(1.2%)

Like the noctule and Leisler's, it hardly ever enters cave-like sites in the winter, and 90% of the records are from the summer months (Figure 14).

Figure 14. Total number of records of pipistrelles for each month

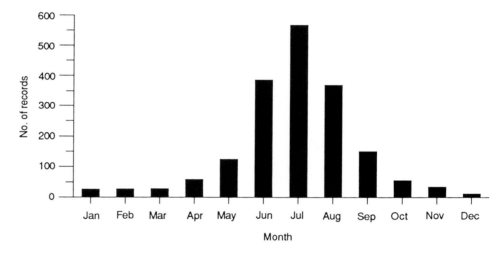

It is widespread over most of Britain and occurs on many of the islands. It does not appear to be resident on the Shetlands - there is one record from 1974.

Barbastelle

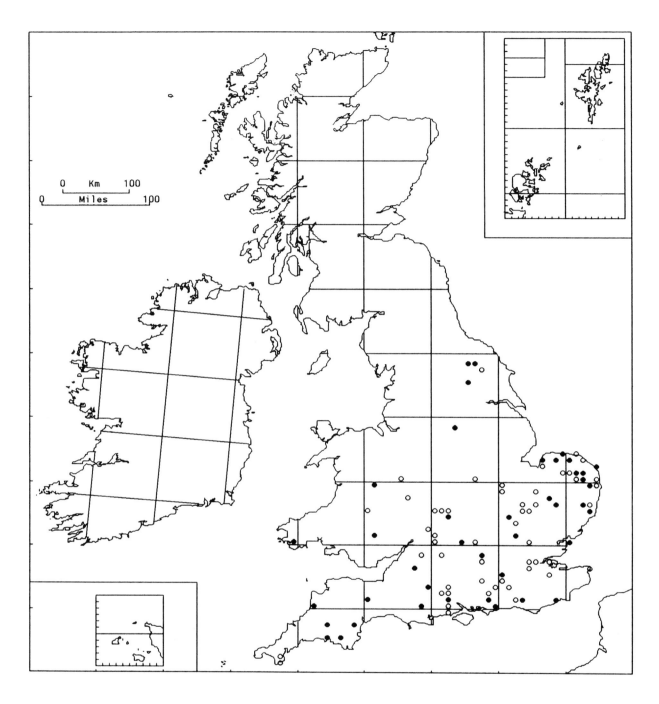

● 1960 onwards   (Great Britain 41, Channel Islands 0)

○ Up to 1959   (Great Britain 52, Channel Islands 0)

Barbastelle (*Barbastella barbastellus* (Schreber 1774))

Handbook 128-130.

Status Native. Rare.

Protection status WCA Schedule 5. BC Appendix II.

Description and recognition With its broad, short ears meeting in the centre of the forehead, and its dark membranes, this bat should be unmistakable.

Very little is known about the species in Britain and it is rarely encountered, although the records are widely spread south of a line from the Mersey to the Tees. No breeding colonies are known and most of the records are of single individuals. It is thought to prefer wooded areas, but in Europe it will use buildings as breeding sites. It hibernates in underground sites and appears to prefer the coldest parts. Two-thirds of the 85 dated records are for the summer months (April-September) but only 20% are in July and August, which are often peak months for other bat species (Figure 15).

Figure 15. Total number of records of barbastelles for each month

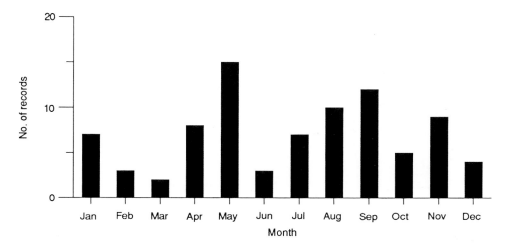

Out of a total of 140 records, 102 include details of the nature of the record:

Museum specimen	38	(37.3%)
In hand	21	(20.6%)
Close sight	12	(11.8%)
Found dead	9	(8.8%)
Road casualty	4	(3.9%)

Despite the recent increased interest in bats, there has not been an increase in the number of records; in fact, there seems to have been a decline in the number of reported occurrences in the last two decades after a peak in the 1950s and 1960s (Figure 16).

Figure 16. Total number of records of barbastelles for each decade since 1841

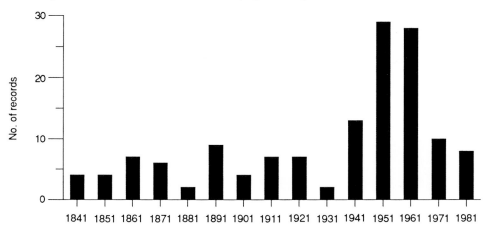

Long-eared bats

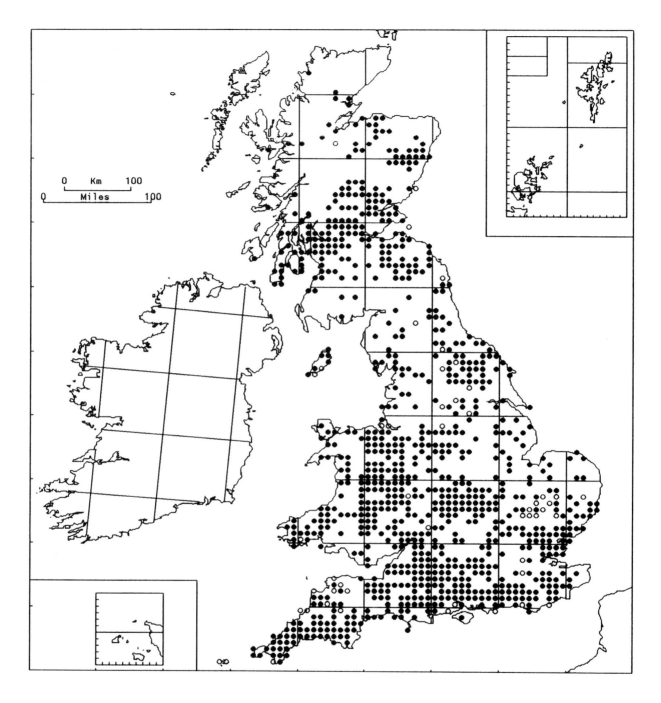

● 1960 onwards   (Great Britain 896, Channel Islands 0)

O Up to 1959   (Great Britain 51, Channel Islands 0)

Long-eared bats

The two species, the grey long-eared and the brown long-eared, are difficult to distinguish, except by accurate measurement of several morphological characters. No one character is sufficient. As far as is known, however, the grey long-eared is only found in a small area of south and south-west England, and it is likely that the vast majority of bats found outside this area belong to the commoner species. Nevertheless, only bats which have been examined in detail have been assigned to one species or the other, and the rest of the records have been mapped as long-eared species.

Brown long-eared bat

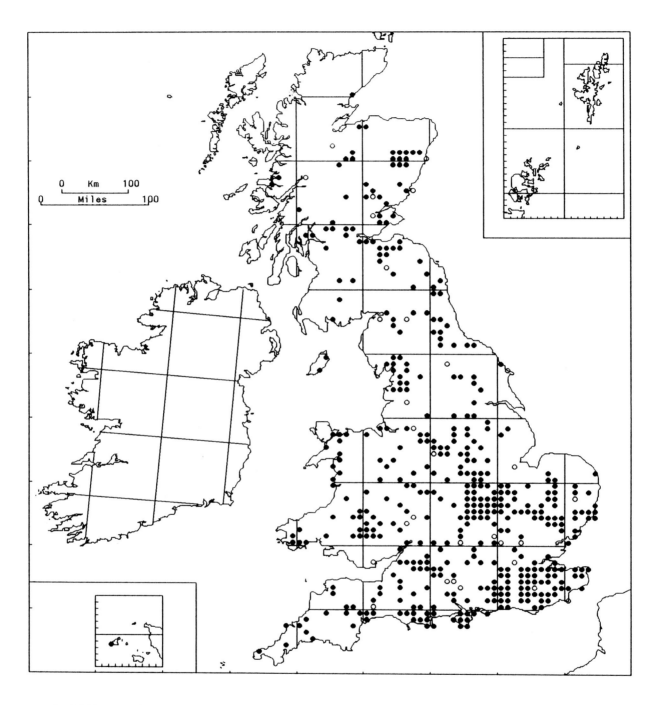

● 1960 onwards   (Great Britain 438, Channel Islands 1)

○ Up to 1959   (Great Britain 30, Channel Islands 0)

Brown long-eared bat (*Plecotus auritus* (L. 1758))

Handbook 131-135.

Status Native. Vulnerable. Declining. Ireland - widespread.

Protection status WCA Schedule 5. BC Appendix II.

Description and recognition The long ears, which meet above the forehead, distinguish this species from all but the grey long-eared bat. There is no simple way to separate the two species, and careful measurement is needed.

This is the next most recorded species of bat after the pipistrelle.

Out of a total of 860 records, 849 include details of the nature of the record:

In hand	349	(41.1%)
Museum specimen	257	(30.3%)
Found dead	134	(15.8%)
Close sight	73	(8.6%)
Cat caught	18	(2.1%)

Although it hibernates in underground sites and is therefore frequently encountered in winter, like the pipistrelle it is also often found roosting in houses where it is seen hanging in attics and other roof voids in the breeding season. Most other bat species, apart from the horseshoe, are not easily seen when roosting in roof spaces. Seventy per cent of the records are from the summer months (Figure 17).

Figure 17. Total number of records of brown long-eared bats for each month

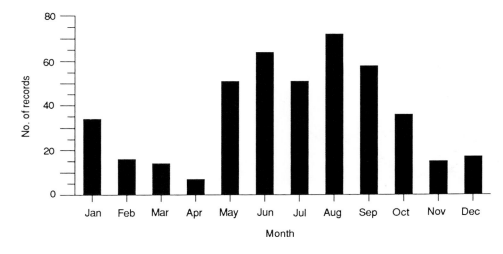

Grey long-eared bat

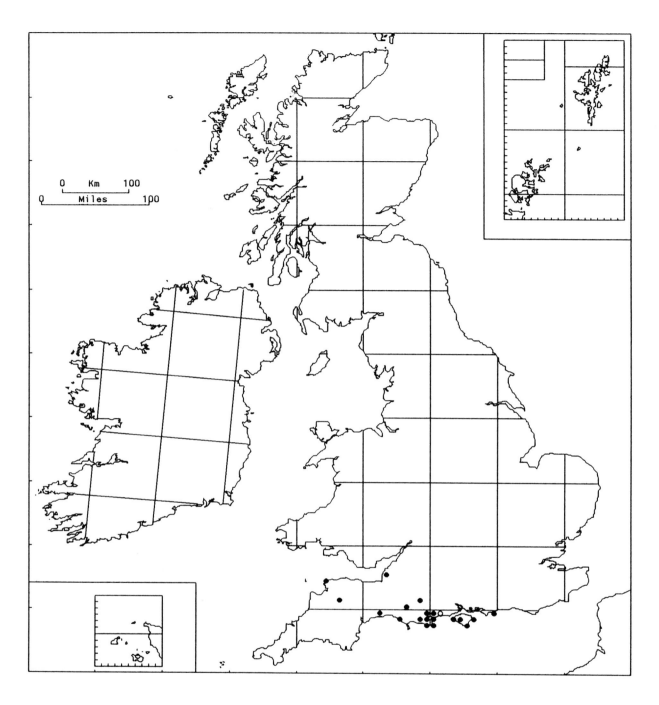

● 1960 onwards   (Great Britain 19, Channel Islands 0)

○ Up to 1959   (Great Britain 2, Channel Islands 1)

Grey long-eared bat (*Plecotus austriacus* (Fischer 1829))

Handbook 135-138.

Status Native. Rare and vulnerable.

Protection status WCA Schedule 5. BC Appendix II.

Description and recognition This species is slightly larger and greyer than the brown long-eared bat, but extremely difficult to distinguish.

It is very similar in all respects to the brown long-eared bat, but is confined to Somerset, Dorset, Devon, Hampshire, the Isle of Wight and Jersey.

Rabbit

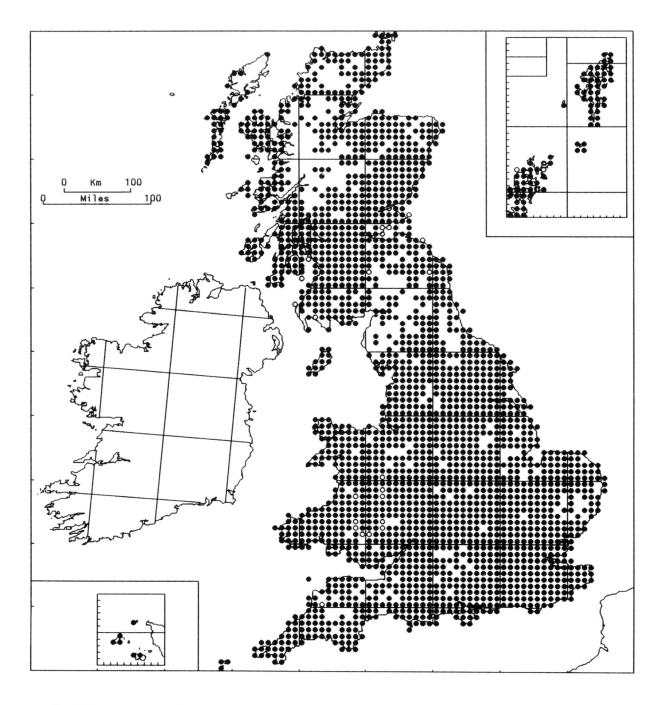

● 1960 onwards   (Great Britain 2261, Channel Islands 6)

○ Up to 1959   (Great Britain 27, Channel Islands 0)

Rabbit (*Oryctolagus cuniculus* L. 1758)

Handbook 146-154.

Status Introduced by the Normans. Common. Increasing. Ireland - common and widespread.

Protection status

Description and recognition With its long ears and short white tail, the rabbit can only be confused with the hare; however, the rabbit's ears do not have black tips.

The rabbit is virtually ubiquitous throughout the mainland, at least below the treeline, and any gaps in the map are almost certainly due to lack of records. As it is such a common and familiar species, it is probably assumed that everything is known about it and amateur naturalists rarely bother to make notes of its occurrence. It has been introduced, or has escaped, on to almost all the small islands that have been inhabited or used by man. They are present on most of the Scilly Islands, where population levels have apparently fluctuated widely, as they have in many parts of the mainland since the introduction of the disease myxomatosis in the 1950s. They are present on the island of Coll (L Rickwood, pers. comm.), but they are now absent from neighbouring Tiree, although they were apparently present on Tiree in the past (Harvie-Brown & Buckley 1892).

Out of a total of 8000 records, 7055 include details of the nature of the record:

Sight	4537	(64.3%)
Road casualty	641	(9.1%)
Faeces	498	(7.1%)
Killed	498	(7.1%)
Burrows	304	(4.3%)
Museum specimen	80	(1.1%)

Records of rabbits rise to a peak in June, when breeding normally ceases, with a slight second peak in September (Figure 18), which is largely due to a high number of road casualties reported in that month (Figure 19).

Figure 18. Total number of records of rabbits for each month

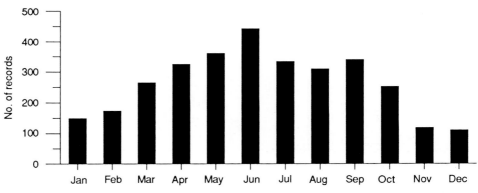

Figure 19. Total number of records of rabbit road casualties for each month

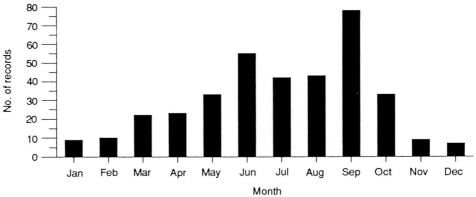

Brown hare

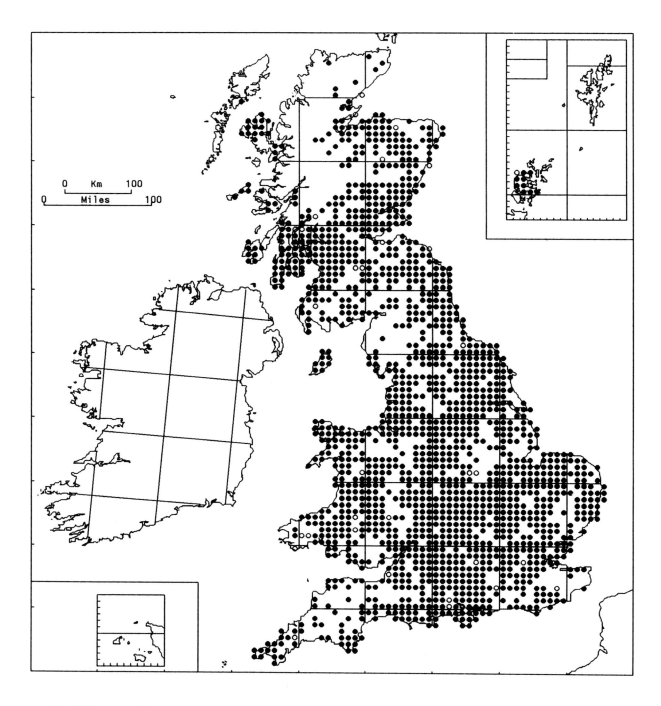

● 1960 onwards   (Great Britain 1603, Channel Islands 0)

○ Up to 1959   (Great Britain 35, Channel Islands 0)

Brown hare (Lepus europaeus Pallas 1778)

Handbook 154-160.

Status Possibly introduced by the Romans. Common. Declining. Ireland - introduced in the 19th century. Uncommon in the north.

Protection status BC Appendix III.

Description and recognition The long black-tipped ears distinguish the brown hare from the rabbit, and the black upper surface of the tail separates it from the mountain hare.

It is widespread in farmland throughout England and Wales and in lowland areas of Scotland, but absent from the north-west and western Highlands. There has been a reduction in numbers of hares since 1960 as shown by the analysis of game bags (Tapper & Parsons 1984), but the reasons for this decline are not known, although it seems likely that changes in agricultural practice are partly responsible. However, hares are still common animals.

Out of a total of 4125 records, 3415 include details of the nature of the record:

Sight	2887	(84.5%)
Road casualty	293	(8.6%)
Found dead	104	(3.0%)
Museum specimen	54	(1.6%)

Road casualties of hares peak in summer-autumn (Figure 20), whereas sightings of live animals peak in the spring (Figure 21), perhaps reflecting the ease with which animals can be seen on arable fields before the crops have grown.

Figure 20. Total number of records of brown hare road casualties for each month

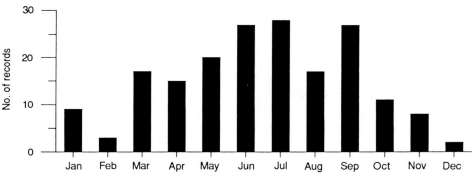

Figure 21. Total number of sight records of brown hare for each month

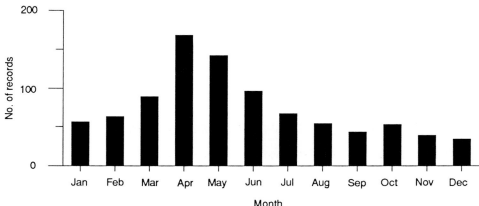

Studies of hare road casualties in Austria and Sweden show similar patterns to the one recorded here (Kutzer & Frey 1981; Goransson & Carlson 1982). It is suggested that this late summer peak occurs when the population is at its highest, and the Austrian study shows that most of the autumn mortality is of inexperienced juvenile animals. The small rise in March may be due to increased activity of hares at the beginning of the mating season

Mountain hare

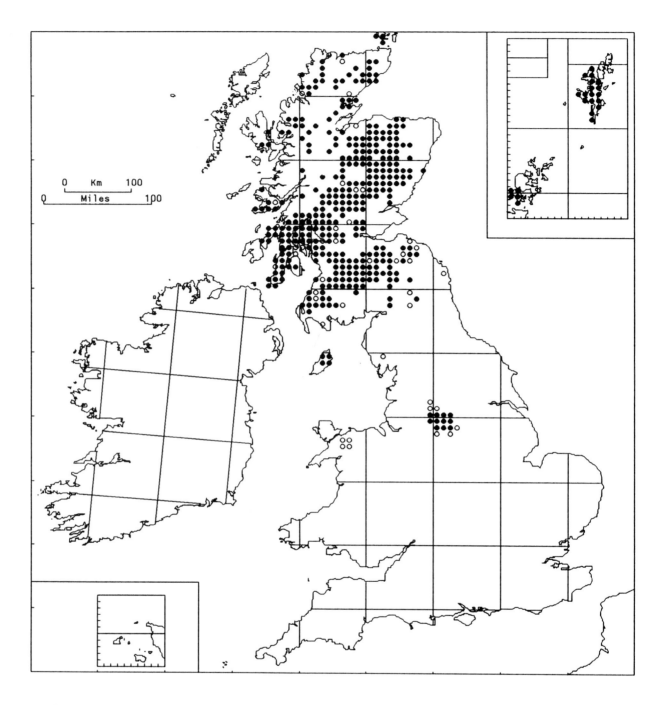

● 1960 onwards   (Great Britain 367, Channel Islands 0)

○ Up to 1959   (Great Britain 45, Channel Islands 0)

Mountain hare (*Lepus timidus* L. 1758)

Handbook 161-167.

Status Native, although some populations introduced. Common where it occurs. Ireland - common and widespread.

Protection status BC Appendix III.

Description and recognition Slightly smaller than the brown hare, the mountain hare has an all-white tail and greyer fur, which sometimes turns white in the winter.

The mountain hare inhabits heather moorland, but its distribution in Britain has been complicated by introductions and reintroductions. The Pennine population originates from about 1880, and the Isle of Man population may have been introduced as recently as 1910 (Fargher 1977). All the island populations are the result of introductions.

Out of a total of 919 records, 647 give details of the nature of the record:

Sight	521	(80.5%)
Museum specimen	60	(9.3%)
Road casualty	35	(5.4%)

Records of the mountain hare rise to a peak in May and then decline to a low point in December (Figure 22).

Figure 22. Total number of records of mountain hares for each month

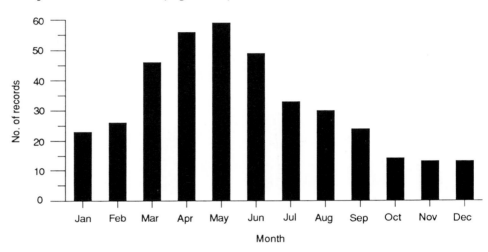

Red squirrel

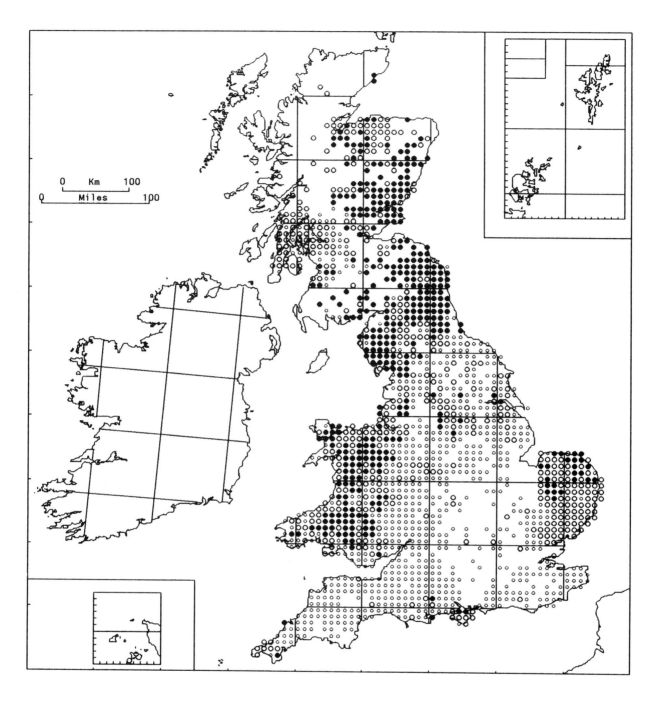

- ● 1975 onwards   (Great Britain 386, Channel Islands 0)

- O 1960–1974 incl.   (Great Britain 450, Channel Islands 2)

- o Up to 1959   (Great Britain 741, Channel Islands 0)

Red squirrel (*Sciurus vulgaris* L. 1758)

Handbook 177-186.

Status Native. Common in Scotland but vulnerable in England and Wales. Declining. Ireland - introduced from Britain in the 19th century. Widespread, but scarce in the west and north.

Protection status WCA Schedule 5. BC Appendix III.

Description and recognition The long bushy tail distinguishes the red squirrel from all but the grey squirrel and the edible dormouse. The red squirrel has a reddish-brown coat, the other two do not. Red squirrels have conspicuous ear tufts in winter.

It is difficult to present the current distribution of this species with any great accuracy as the picture has changed radically in the last two decades but has not been matched with an even effort in recording. The change has been particularly noticeable in East Anglia where the grey squirrel has spread rapidly and the red has declined since the early 1960s. There are few places in southern England where one can still find red squirrels, although they are still present on the Isle of Wight, and Brownsea Island in Poole Harbour.

Out of a total of 4841 records, 1483 include details of the nature of the record:

Sight	1209	(81.5%)
Museum specimen	137	(9.2%)
Feeding signs	40	(2.7%)
Road casualty	34	(2.3%)
Killed	31	(2.1%)
Found dead	22	(1.5%)

There are peaks in the number of sightings of red squirrels in April, July and September (Figure 23).

Figure 23. Total number of sight records of red squirrels for each month

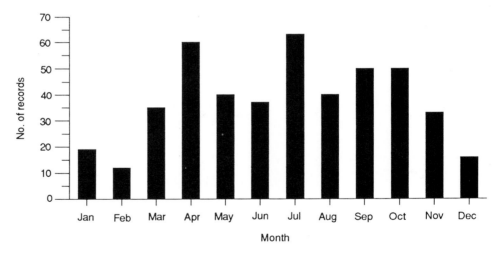

Grey squirrel

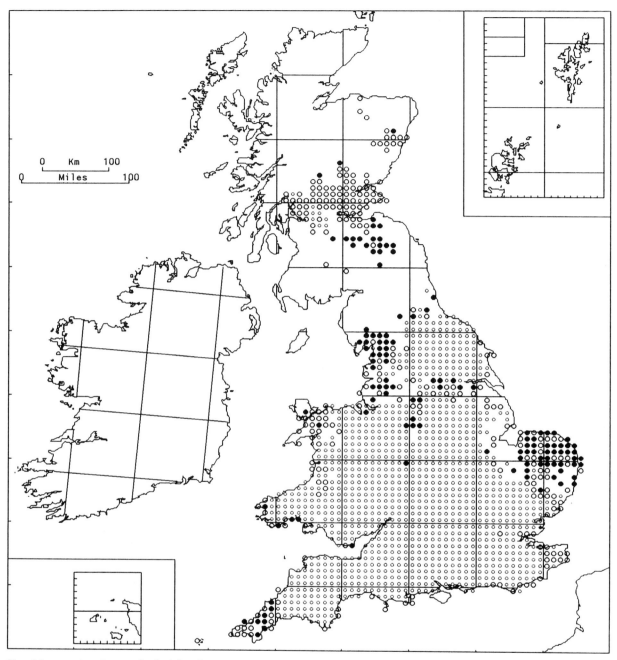

For this species the period of the first record has been mapped, to give an indication of the recent spread.

● 1975 onwards   (Great Britain 124, Channel Islands 0)

O 1960–1974 incl.   (Great Britain 268, Channel Islands 0)

o Up to 1959   (Great Britain 1084, Channel Islands 0)

Grey squirrel (*Sciurus carolinensis* Gmelin 1788)

Handbook 186-191.

Status Introduced between 1870 and 1930. Common. Increasing. Ireland - introduced in 1911. Spreading from the central eastern area.

Protection status

Description and recognition This animal is larger than the red squirrel, with no conspicuous ear tufts. Its fur is mainly grey but with some brown on the back and side, particularly in summer. Black varieties are occasionally seen, as are white ones.

From the many introductions in the late 19th and early 20th centuries, the grey squirrel has done extremely well. It occupies most of England and Wales, and is continuing to spread in Scotland. One of the last areas to be occupied in England, the north-west, is gradually being colonised. A Grey Squirrel Control Society was formed in the area in the late 1980s in an attempt to halt the spread, but, although it may have slowed down the rate of colonisation, it has certainly not stopped it.

Out of a total of 5483 records, 3427 include details of the nature of the record:

Sight	2812	(82.1%)
Road casualty	197	(5.7%)
Killed	112	(3.3%)
Found dead	105	(3.1%)
Museum specimen	102	(3.0%)
Nest	46	(1.3%)

Recorded sightings of grey squirrels peak in April, June and October (Figure 24).

Figure 24. Total number of sight records of grey squirrels for each month

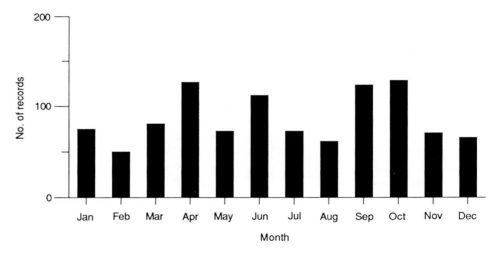

Bank vole

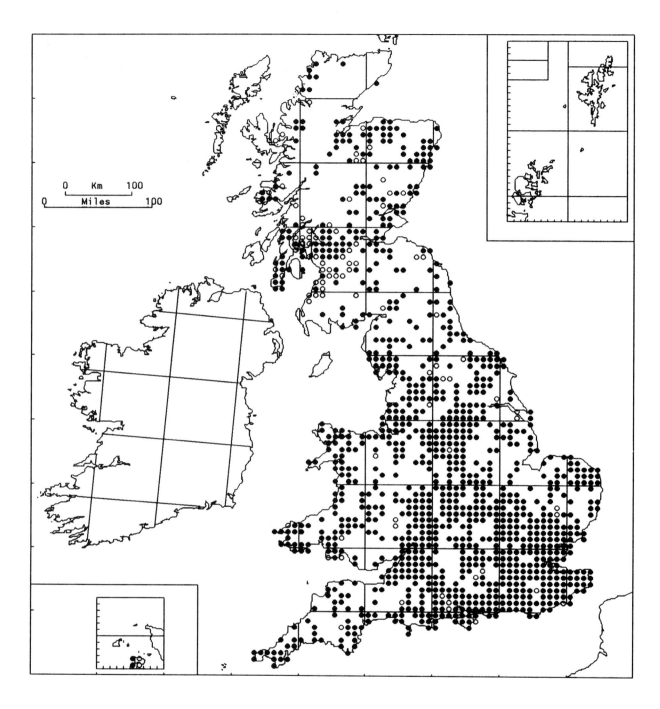

● 1960 onwards   (Great Britain 1062, Channel Islands 2)

○ Up to 1959   (Great Britain 86, Channel Islands 2)

Bank vole (*Clethrionomys glareolus* (Schreber 1780))

Handbook 192-202.

Status Native. Abundant. Ireland - probably introduced about 1950. Confined to the south-west but spreading.

Protection status

Description and recognition The bank vole is not always easy to separate from the field vole, but its chestnut fur and longer tail (about 50% of head and body length) should enable it to be distinguished if a close enough view is obtained.

It is widespread throughout Britain, but rather under-recorded, perhaps because of the above-mentioned confusion with the field vole.

Out of a total of 2246 records, 1831 include details of the nature of the record:

Trapped	689	(37.6%)
In bottle	382	(20.9%)
Bird pellet	256	(14.0%)
Sight	174	(9.5%)
Museum specimen	153	(8.4%)
Found dead	73	(4.0%)
Cat kill	52	(2.8%)
Road casualty	20	(1.1%)

The monthly number of records peaks in April and September (Figure 25).

Figure 25. Total number of records of bank vole for each month

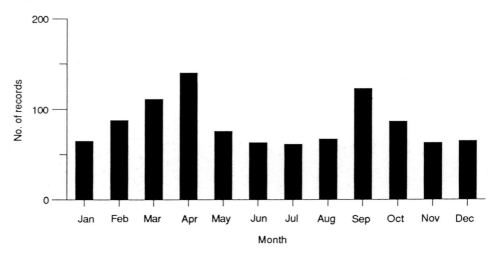

Bank voles were found between 1966 and 1970 in the Brodick Castle area of Arran, probably the result of an unrecorded recent introduction (Gibson 1973). There is an unconfirmed record from Islay from 1974.

Field vole

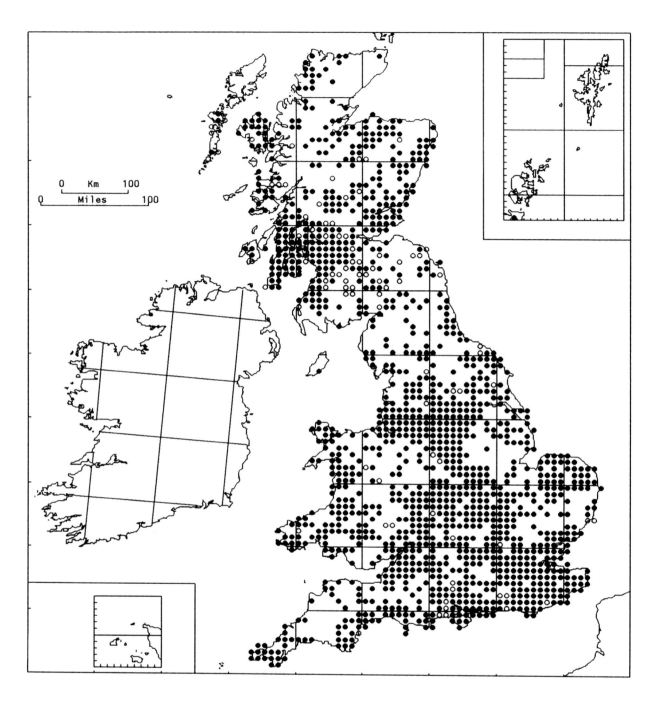

● 1960 onwards   (Great Britain 1302, Channel Islands 0)

○ Up to 1959   (Great Britain 85, Channel Islands 0)

Field vole (*Microtus agrestis* (L. 1761)

Handbook 203-208.

Status Native. Abundant.

Protection status

Description and recognition The field vole can usually be distinguished from the bank vole by its yellow-brown fur and its rather shorter tail (about 30% of head and body length).

It is mainly found in open grassland, but also in areas such as young forestry plantations and hedgerows. Like the bank vole, it is rather under-recorded.

Out of a total of 2737 records, 2178 include details of the nature of the record:

Bird pellet	470	(21.6%)
Trapped	468	(21.5%)
Sight	310	(14.2%)
Museum specimen	243	(11.2%)
Found dead	212	(9.7%)
In bottle	196	(9.0%)
Cat kill	84	(3.9%)
Holes	56	(2.6%)
Faeces	47	(2.2%)
Road casualty	30	(1.4%)

Numbers of records peak in spring and mid-summer (Figure 26).

Figure 26. Total number of records of field vole for each month

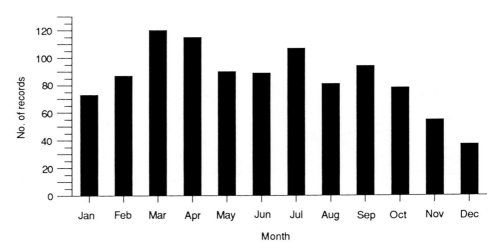

Orkney and Guernsey field vole

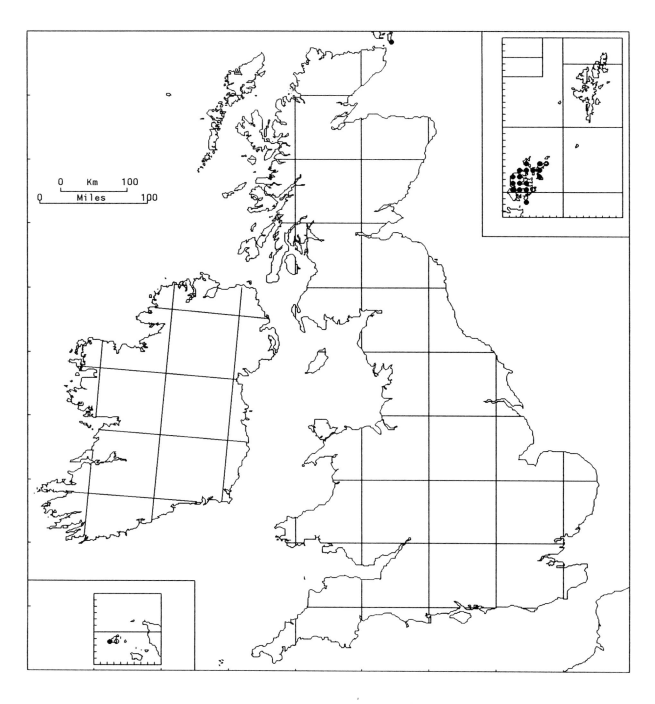

● 1960 onwards   (Great Britain 16, Channel Islands 1)

○ Up to 1959   (Great Britain 2, Channel Islands 1)

Orkney and Guernsey field vole (*Microtus arvalis* (Pallas 1779)

Handbook 208-211.

Status Orkney -
introduced *c* 3500 BC;
Guernsey - possibly
introduced. Very common
where it occurs.

Protection status

Description and recognition It is the only vole found on those islands
on which it occurs, so no identification problems exist.

It is restricted to Guernsey and the following Orkney islands: South
Ronaldsay, Mainland, Rousay, Westray, Stronsay, Sanday. There are two
records from Eday - remains from a long-eared owl pellet in 1965, and a
reported introduction of a few voles from Westray in 1987 and 1988.

Water vole

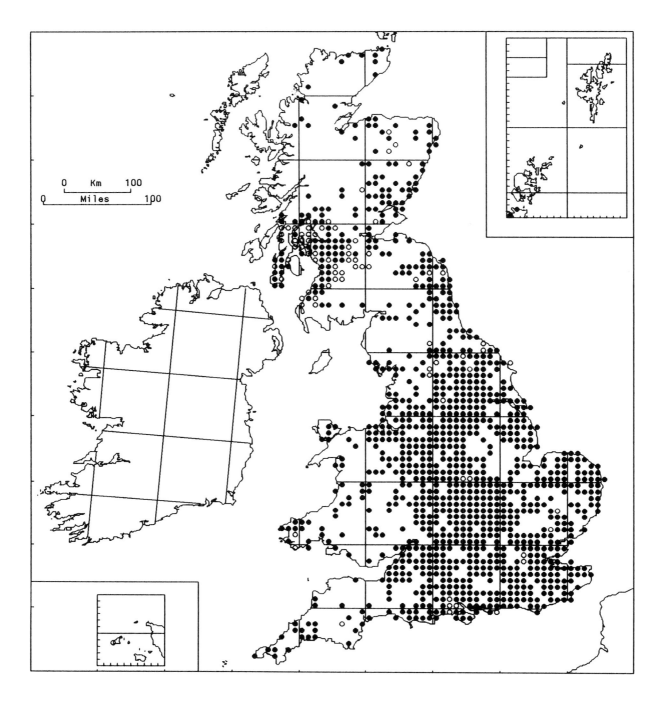

● 1960 onwards   (Great Britain 1060, Channel Islands 0)

○ Up to 1959   (Great Britain 78, Channel Islands 1)

Water vole (*Arvicola terrestris* (L. 1758))

Handbook 212-218.

Status Native. Common. Declining?

Protection status

Description and recognition This vole is sometimes referred to as the water rat but should not be confused with the true rats. Its blunt muzzle, less conspicuous ears, and shorter, hairier tail distinguish it from the brown rat.

It is mainly confined to low ground and usually, although not always, near water. Some recent studies have shown declines in water vole numbers with the arrival of the American mink, but there is no obvious reduction in range of the water vole.

Out of a total of 3007 records, 2273 include details of the nature of the record:

Sight	1729	(76.1%)
Faeces	203	(8.9%)
Museum specimen	85	(3.7%)
Trapped	51	(2.2%)
Found dead	29	(1.3%)
Tracks	29	(1.3%)
Cat kill	24	(1.1%)

The number of records per month steadily increases through the first half of the year and peaks in June-July, after which it declines to a low level in winter (Figure 27). This reflects quite accurately the low level of water vole activity in the winter months.

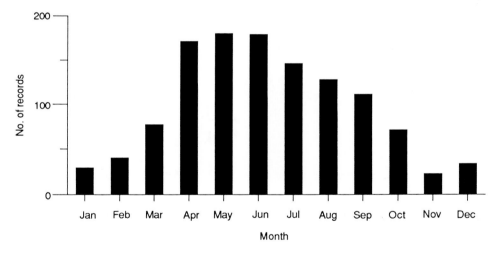

Figure 27. Total number of records of water vole for each month

Wood mouse

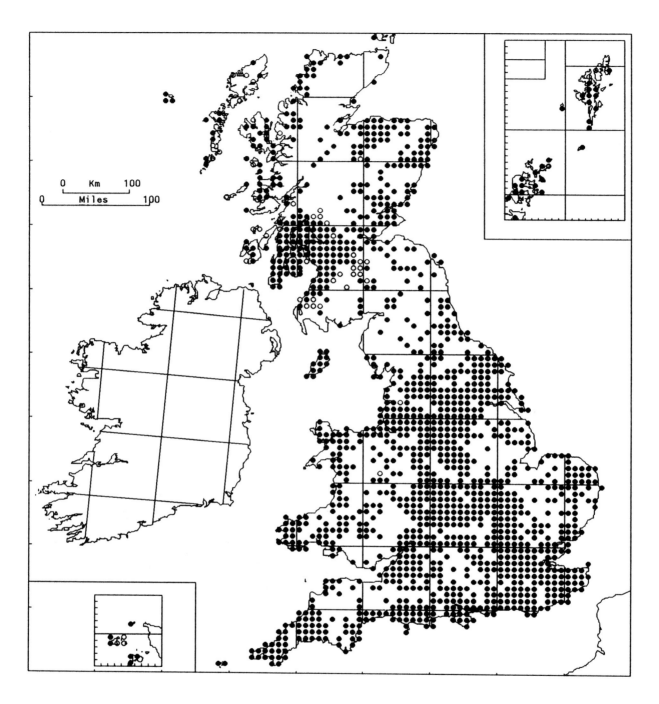

● 1960 onwards   (Great Britain 1373, Channel Islands 6)

○ Up to 1959   (Great Britain 45, Channel Islands 3)

Wood mouse (*Apodemus sylvaticus* (L.1758))

Handbook 220-229.

Status Native. Abundant.
Ireland - widespread.

Protection status

Description and recognition The wood mouse, with its brown upper fur, pale grey underside, large black eyes, large furless ears and pointed nose is easily recognised.

It is the most common small rodent in Britain, and occurs in most habitats where there is cover. It is found on many small islands, and many of these populations have been studied in detail in an effort to determine the route through which they arrived. Both non-metric and genetic variation have been used in this work. Most of these small island populations have arrived with man, usually accidentally.

Out of a total of 2635 records, 1892 include details of the nature of the record:

Trapped	863	(45.6%)
Sight	223	(11.8%)
found dead	191	(10.1%)
Bird pellet	183	(9.7%)
Museum specimen	179	(9.5%)
In bottle	138	(7.3%)
Cat kill	66	(3.5%)
Road casualty	23	(1.2%)

There are two peaks in the numbers of records collected, in March-April and in September (Figure 28).

Figure 28. Total number of records of wood mouse for each month

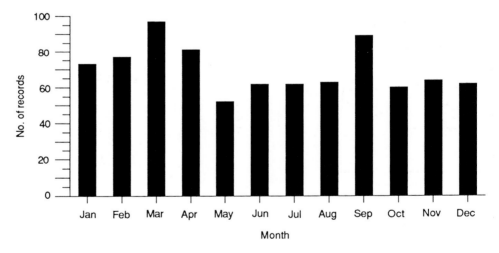

Yellow-necked mouse

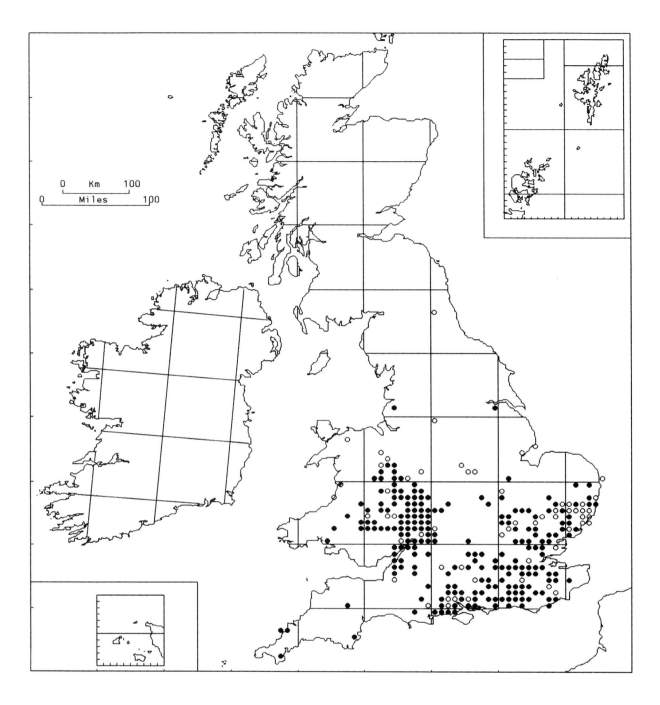

●   Post 1960   (Great Britain 214, Channel Islands 0)

O   Pre 1959   (Great Britain 58, Channel Islands 0)

Yellow-necked mouse (*Apodemus flavicollis* (Melchior 1834))

Handbook 229-233

Status Native. Common where it occurs.

Protection status

Description and recognition The yellow-necked mouse is very similar to the wood mouse but is slightly larger and has a band of yellow-brown fur under the neck which joins the brown upper fur. It is also more brightly coloured above and whiter below than the wood mouse.

It is primarily a woodland species. It is said to be renowned for entering houses (Flowerdew 1984) and, out of 52 records where information was given, 25 were from inside houses, compared with two out of 107 for wood mice, although the wood mouse undoubtedly enters houses more frequently than that figure suggests. The distribution of the yellow-necked mouse is still not fully explained, although it may be related partly to ancient woodland areas. There is some support for this theory in that, taking a list of 50 species defined in the literature as inhabiting ancient woodland, the average number of these species which occurs in squares in which the yellow-necked mouse is recorded is 19.1, whereas the average number which occurs in squares where the species is not recorded (within the range of the mouse) is 12.9. The average number of ancient woodland species in squares containing wood mice is 13.7.

Out of a total of 487 records, 345 include details of the nature of the record:

Trapped	212	(61.4%)
Museum specimen	66	(19.1%)
Found dead	25	(7.2%)
Sight	17	(4.9%)
Cat kill	12	(3.5%)
In bottle	7	(2.0%)

Harvest mouse

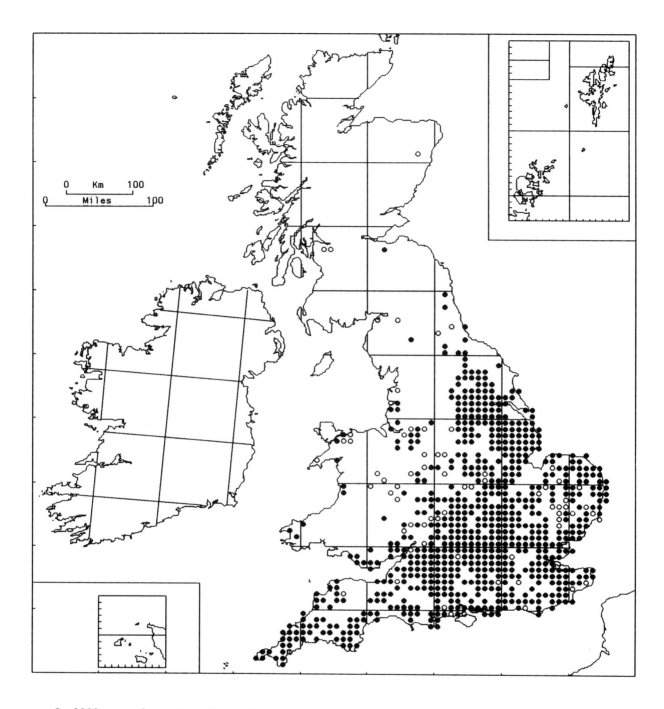

● 1960 onwards   (Great Britain 693, Channel Islands 0)

○ Up to 1959   (Great Britain 70, Channel Islands 0)

Harvest mouse (*Micromys minutus* (Pallas 1771))

Handbook 233-239.

Status Native. Common but local.

Protection status

Description and recognition Its small size, and reddish-orange dorsal fur should identify this species. It has a long, prehensile tail. It is the smallest rodent in Britain.

Out of a total of 1341 records, 1051 include details of the nature of the record:

Nest	524	(49.9%)
Sight	155	(14.7%)
Bird pellet	128	(12.2%)
Trapped	127	(12.1%)
Found dead	38	(3.6%)
Cat kill	37	(3.5%)
Museum specimen	18	(1.7%)

Although easily recognised by its colour and small size, in a Mammal Society survey Harris (1979) showed that this mouse is most easily located by the characteristic nests that it constructs, and a high proportion of records are of nests. The nests are made from woven grass leaves which are left attached to the plant and remain green for some time, camouflaged by the surrounding vegetation. Hence, they are not easy to find during the summer, but in the winter they become much more visible (Figure 29) as round balls of dry leaves suspended amongst the grassy stems.

Figure 29. Total number of records of harvest mouse nests for each month

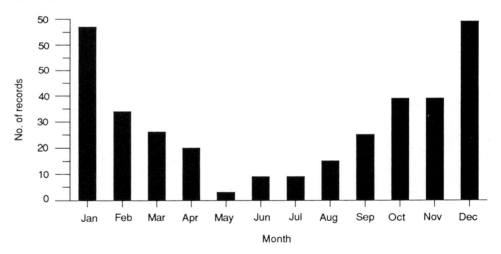

Few records are derived from live trapping as harvest mice are generally too light to trigger the mechanism on a standard mammal trap, unless it is set very lightly.

It is reputed to occur on the Isle of Wight, but it has not been possible to confirm this.

House mouse

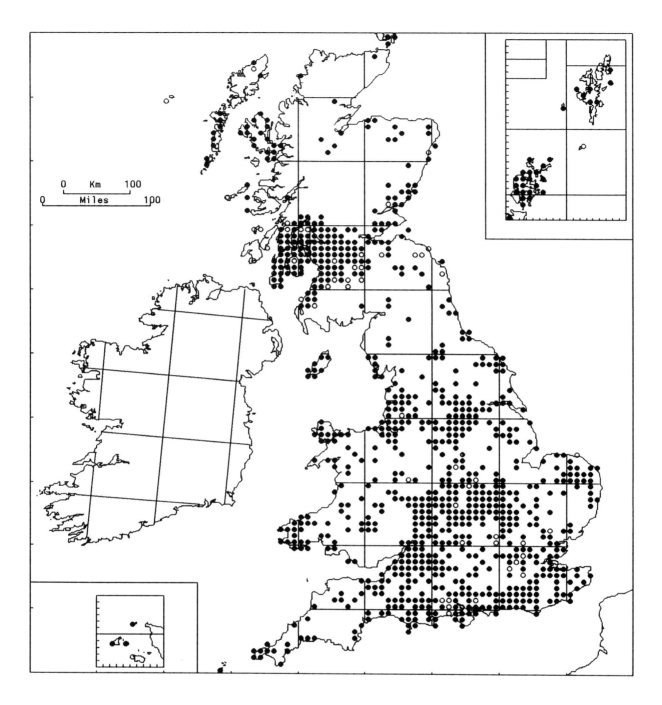

● 1960 onwards   (Great Britain 3440, Channel Islands 12)

○ Up to 1959   (Great Britain 220, Channel Islands 4)

House mouse (*Mus domesticus* Rutty 1772)

Handbook 239-247.

Status Probably
introduced. Common.
Ireland - widespread and
common.

Protection status

Description and recognition Although sometimes confused with the
wood mouse, the house mouse is much greyer, both above and below,
than that species. It has a characteristic strong 'mousy' smell.

It is assumed to be ubiquitous throughout Britain and is therefore
seriously under-recorded; it is presumably ignored because of its
familiarity. Although mainly found in buildings and food or grain stores, it
will also occur out of doors, and of course not all mice found in houses
are house mice.

Out of a total of 1463 records, 1030 include details of the nature of the
record:

Trapped	376	(36.5%)
Sight	189	(18.3%)
Found dead	175	(17.0%)
Bird pellet	129	(12.5%)
Museum specimen	88	(8.5%)
Cat kill	26	(2.5%)
Faeces	21	(2.0%)
In bottle	14	(1.4%)

There appears to be little clear pattern in the monthly numbers of records
(Figure 30), which is perhaps a reflection of the patchy nature of the
recording of this species.

Figure 30. Total number of
records of house mouse for
each month

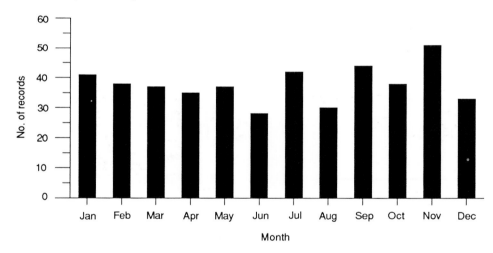

Brown rat

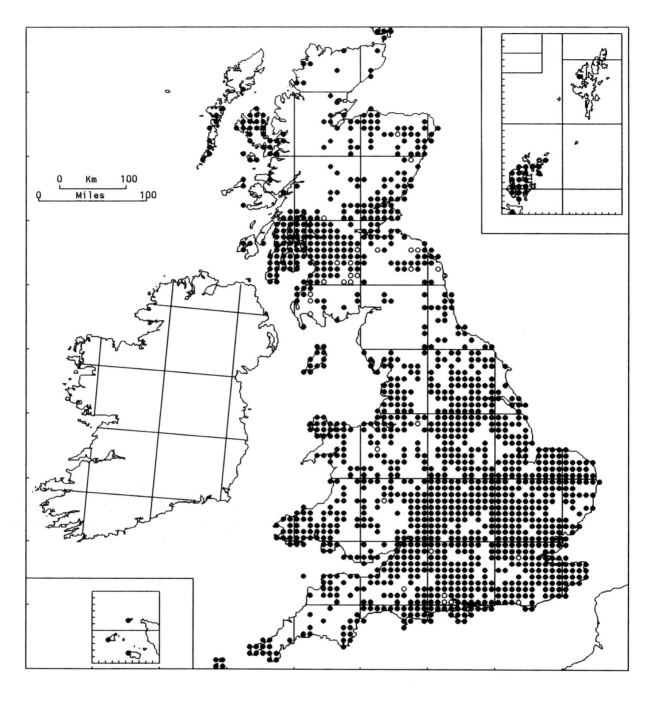

● 1960 onwards   (Great Britain 1391, Channel Islands 3)

○ Up to 1959   (Great Britain 32, Channel Islands 0)

Brown rat (*Rattus norvegicus* (Berkenhout 1769))

Handbook 248-255.

Status Introduced *c* 1728. Common. Ireland - common and widespread.

Protection status

Description and recognition The brown rat is a large (280 mm head and body) rodent with a scaly tail and finely furry ears.

Like the house mouse, this species is presumed to be ubiquitous but is under-recorded in many areas. It is another species that establishes itself almost everywhere man settles and has reached many islands, although there are few records from the Shetlands or the Outer Hebrides.

Out of a total of 2946 records, 2313 include details of the nature of the record:

Sight	978	(42.3%)
Road casualty	563	(24.3%)
Found dead	328	(14.2%)
Killed	105	(4.5%)
Faeces	83	(3.6%)
Bird pellet	73	(3.2%)
Museum specimen	66	(2.9%)
Trapped	57	(2.6%)
Cat kill	18	(0.8%)

The numbers of records of brown rat peak in spring and late autumn (Figure 31).

Figure 31. Total number of records of brown rat for each month

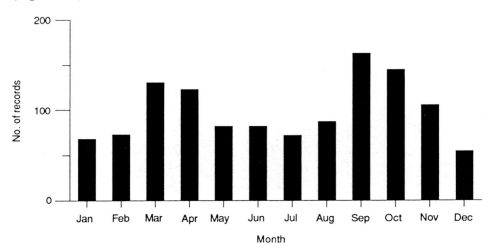

Black rat

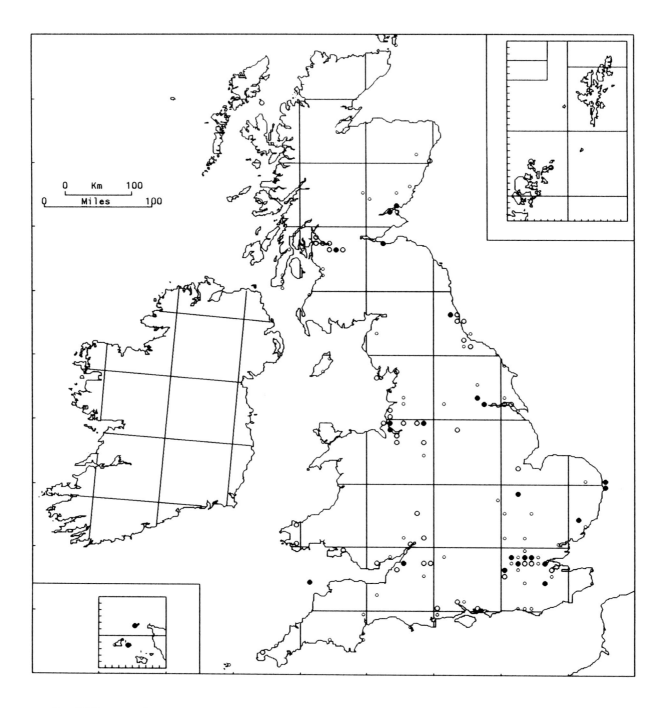

● 1975 onwards   (Great Britain 23, Channel Islands 2)

O 1960–1974 incl.   (Great Britain 48, Channel Islands 0)

o Up to 1959   (Great Britain 71, Channel Islands 2)

Black rat (*Rattus rattus* (L. 1758))

Handbook 255-259.

Status Introduced at least as early as 3rd century; continual further introductions from ships. Vulnerable. Declining. Ireland - confined to a few ports.

Protection status

Description and recognition The black rat is a large (240 mm head and body) rodent with a scaly tail and almost furless ears. Its tail is longer and thinner than that of the brown rat.

It is not always easy to distinguish black rats from brown rats, especially as melanistic forms of the brown rat occur, as do brown forms of the black rat, so fur colour is by no means diagnostic. Only a few black rats remain in Britain and it is perhaps doubtful whether any self-sustaining colonies exist on the mainland, although they are still present on Lundy and on Sark. They are mostly confined to busy ports, although some recent records have been from isolated food warehouses (Twigg 1992), and have presumably been transported on lorries, possibly in containers.

Dormouse

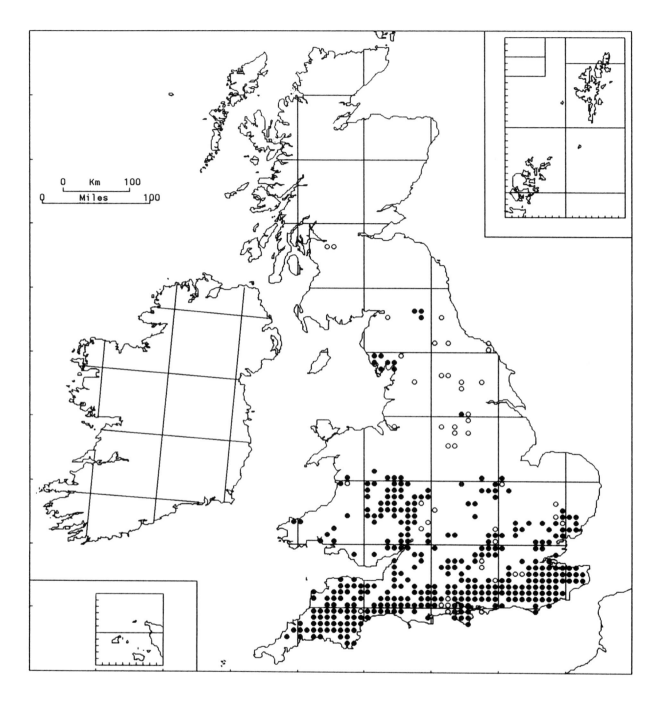

● 1960 onwards   (Great Britain 352, Channel Islands 0)

○ Up to 1959   (Great Britain 46, Channel Islands 0)

Dormouse (*Muscardinus avellanarius* L. 1758)

Handbook 259-264.

Status Native. Uncommon, local. Has declined.

Protection status WCA Schedule 5, 6. BC Appendix III.

Description and recognition A small golden-brown mouse with a thickly furry tail, it is sometimes known as the common or hazel dormouse to distinguish it from the European species, although 'common' is hardly appropriate.

The presence of the dormouse is most easily established by looking for hazel nuts on which it has fed. The neat, round hole with the smooth cut edge and the oblique tooth marks on the shell surface are distinctive. Although it has certainly declined in abundance in the past 100 years, and has lost ground in northern England where it was not very common in the 19th century, there is no evidence of any major change in range over the past 30 years and it still survives in areas of suitable habitat. Recent surveys have established that some northern populations still exist, and it may still be present in some of the areas where there are only 19th century records available. Like the yellow-necked mouse (qv), it seems to be associated with ancient woodland, the average 'score' for squares with dormice being 19.7. The average score for squares with both dormice and yellow-necked mice is 21.8.

Out of a total of 796 records, 677 include details of the nature of the record:

Chewed nuts	278	(41.1%)
Sight	234	(34.6%)
Nests	68	(10.0%)
Trapped	34	(5.0%)
Museum specimen	23	(3.4%)
Found dead	16	(2.4%)
Bird pellet	8	(1.2%)
Cat kill	6	(0.9%)

Fat dormouse

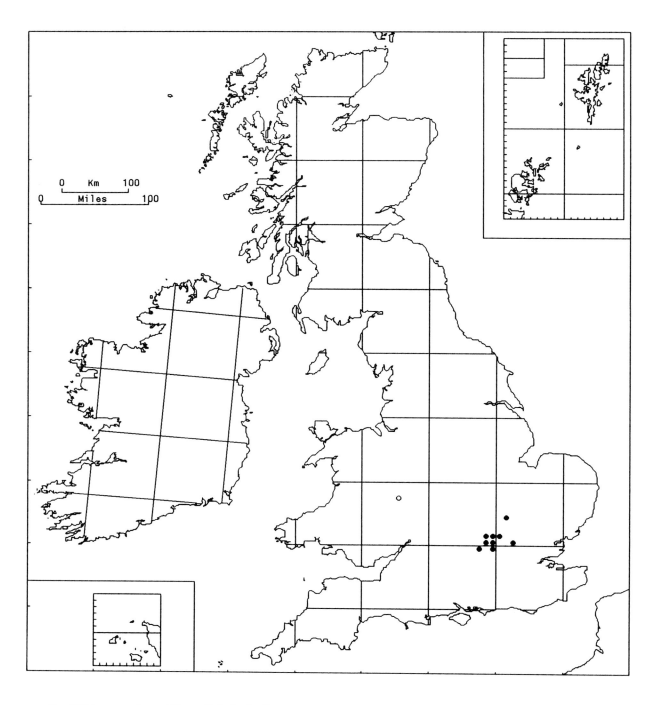

● 1960 onwards   (Great Britain 9, Channel Islands 0)

○ Up to 1959   (Great Britain 1, Channel Islands 0)

Fat dormouse (*Glis glis* (L. 1766))

Handbook 264-267.

Status Introduced 1902. Uncommon.

Protection status WCA Schedule 6. BC Appendix III.

Description and recognition The only other rodents in Britain with thickly furry tails are the squirrels. The fat dormouse is much smaller than the squirrel, and it has a shorter muzzle and rounded, short ears.

The fat or edible dormouse has hardly spread from its original introduction site at Tring in Hertfordshire. The presence of outlying records at Ludlow and in Wiltshire and Worcestershire (which cannot be mapped because the localities are not precisely known) suggests that the Tring introductions were not the only ones. The outlying record at Sandy (TL14) dates from 1974. In some places it achieves pest status, either by causing damage to young trees in plantations, or by entering attics and outbuildings, causing disturbance and damage, especially to stored fruit.

Coypu

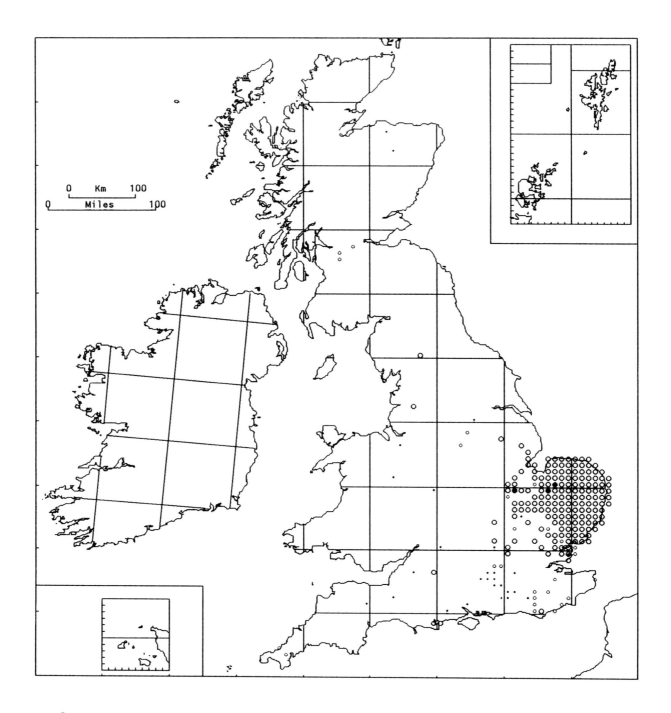

● 1988 onwards   (Great Britain 3, Channel Islands 0)

○ 1965–1987 incl.   (Great Britain 169, Channel Islands 0)

○ 1945–1964 incl.   (Great Britain 27, Channel Islands 0)

• Up to 1945   (Great Britain 28, Channel Islands 0)

Coypu (*Myocastor coypus* (Molina) 1782)

Handbook 267-275.

Status Introduced 1930s.
Probably extinct (1990).
Severely controlled.

Protection status

Description and recognition This coypu is a large rodent with a blunt muzzle, webbed hind feet, and large orange incisors.

The coypu was introduced to Britain for its fur (nutria) in the 1930s, and numerous escapes occurred, although it only established itself in two areas: at a sewage farm near Slough where a colony existed from 1940 to 1954, and in East Anglia, centred in the Norfolk Broads area. Its spread in Britain since its escape has been well documented (eg Lever 1979). Although vulnerable to harsh winters, it was able to recover rapidly from such setbacks until a carefully planned trapping campaign was instituted in the 1980s, and it is now believed to have been eliminated from Britain (Gosling & Baker 1989) after a determined effort of concentrated trapping in the highest density areas.

Out of a total of 1668 records, 1204 include details of the nature of the record:

Trapped	1158	(96.2%)
Sight	23	(1.9%)

Fox

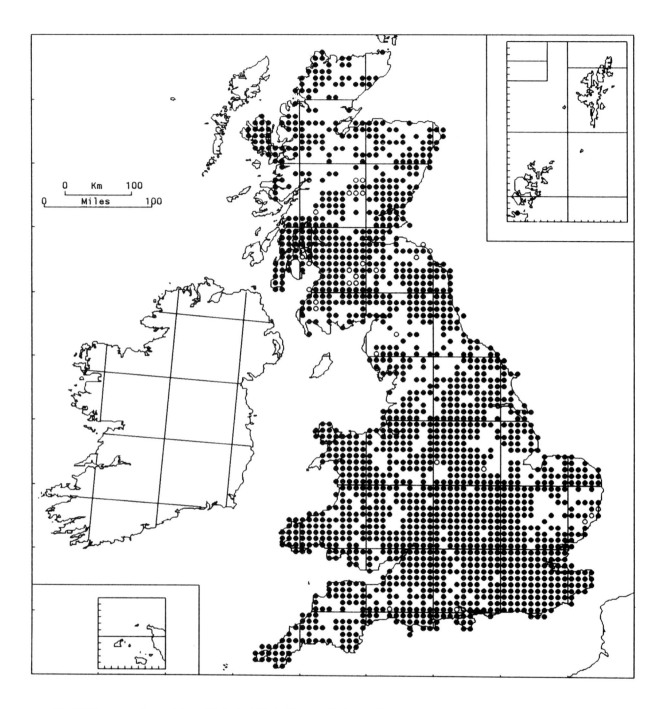

● 1960 onwards (Great Britain 1744, Channel Islands 0)

○ Up to 1959 (Great Britain 32, Channel Islands 0)

Fox (*Vulpes vulpes* (L. 1758))

Handbook 351-367.

Status Native. Common. Ireland - common and widespread.

Protection status

Description and recognition This large, dog-like carnivore has a long bushy tail, often with a white tip.

The fox is widespread throughout Britain. It appears to be particularly under-recorded in East Anglia.

Out of a total of 5032 records, 3962 include details of the nature of the record:

Sight	2175	(54.9%)
Killed	486	(12.3%)
Faeces	438	(11.1%)
Tracks	198	(5.0%)
Road casualty	191	(4.8%)
Found dead	188	(4.7%)
Museum specimen	85	(2.1%)
Holes	61	(1.5%)
Scent	46	(1.2%)
Heard	32	(0.8%)

Sightings of foxes peak in May (Figure 32), whilst records of foxes based on other than sightings peak in April (Figure 33).

Figure 32. Total number of sight records of foxes for each month

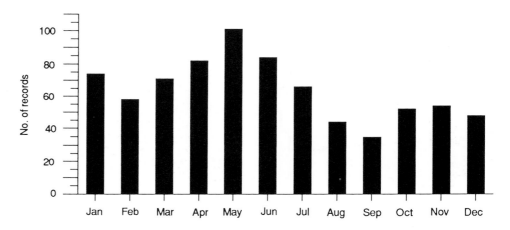

Figure 33. Total number of records, other than sightings, of foxes for each month

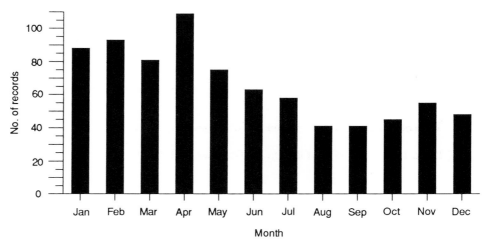

The higher numbers of records in the winter months probably relate to the sexual activity of foxes at that time.

Pine marten

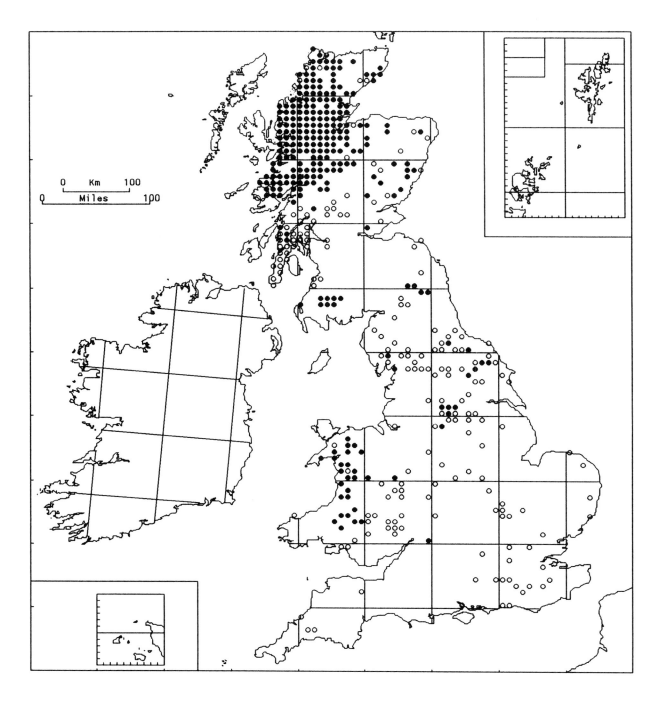

●   1960 onwards   (Great Britain 262, Channel Islands 0)

O   Up to 1959   (Great Britain 183, Channel Islands 0)

Pine marten (*Martes martes* L. 1758)

Handbook 368-376.

Status Native. Uncommon; low density. Increasing range. Ireland - found in forested and rocky areas.

Protection status WCA Schedule 5, 6. BC Appendix III.

Description and recognition The pine marten is a large, long-bodied carnivore with a more upright stance than the other mustelids. It has a long bushy tail.

A survey in 1980-82 (Velander 1983) showed that the pine marten was spreading from its base in the Scottish Highlands, a spread which should continue, given the availability of suitable habitat.

Out of a total of 920 records, 318 include details of the nature of the record:

Sight	118	(37.1%)
Killed	74	(23.3%)
Faeces	44	(13.8%)
Museum specimen	43	(13.5%)
Road casualty	11	(3.5%)
Found dead	11	(3.5%)

Mixed conifer plantations seem to be utilised by pine martens most frequently, although they are found in a wide variety of other habitats. There are still isolated populations in England and Wales, and there are some isolated records of single individuals which appear well founded but may not relate to breeding populations. It is possible that animals may be being translocated. One recent (1981) unconfirmed record from Surrey is not mapped, and Velander mentions other unconfirmed records for Surrey. Most of the pre-1960 records mapped are 19th century records; there are many more records in the literature that have not been extracted.

Stoat

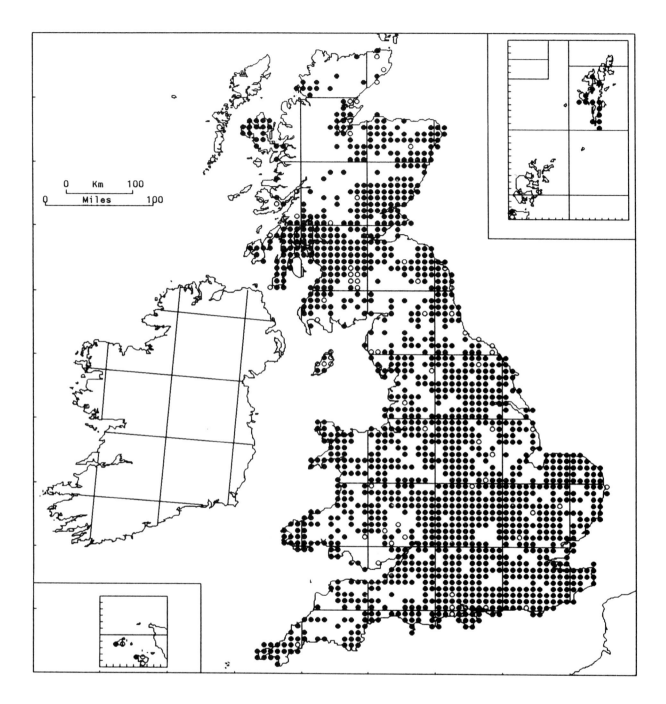

● 1960 onwards (Great Britain 1517, Channel Islands 2)

○ Up to 1959 (Great Britain 68, Channel Islands 3)

Stoat (*Mustela erminea* L. 1758)

Handbook 377-387.

Status Native. Common. Increasing. Ireland - widespread.

Protection status BC Appendix III.

Description and recognition The bright, reddish-brown colour of the dorsal fur, and the long (*c* 40% head and body) tail with its black tip distinguishes the stoat from the other small mustelid carnivore, the weasel.

The stoat is rather under-recorded for an animal that is relatively easily seen, although of course there may be problems in distinguishing stoats from weasels for less experienced observers.

Out of a total of 3515 records, 2625 include details of the nature of the record:

Sight	1781	(67.8%)
Museum specimen	261	(9.9%)
Road casualty	201	(7.7%)
Killed	168	(6.4%)
Found dead	152	(5.8%)
Faeces	23	(0.9%)
Cat kill	12	(0.5%)

One stoat was recorded from a tawny owl pellet.

Sightings of stoats peak in April and August (Figure 34); the April peak may relate to the sexual activity of the adults, and the August peak to dispersal of young animals. Non-sighting records of stoats follow a similar pattern (Figure 35).

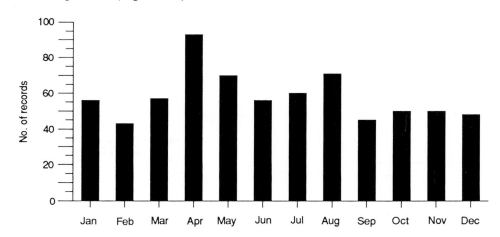

Figure 34. Total number of sight records of stoats for each month

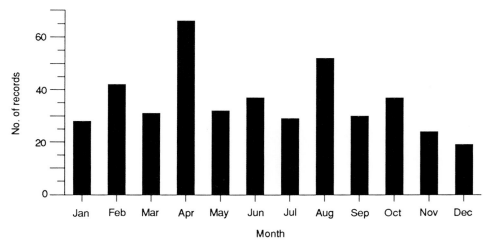

Figure 35. Total number of records, other than sightings, of stoats for each month

Weasel

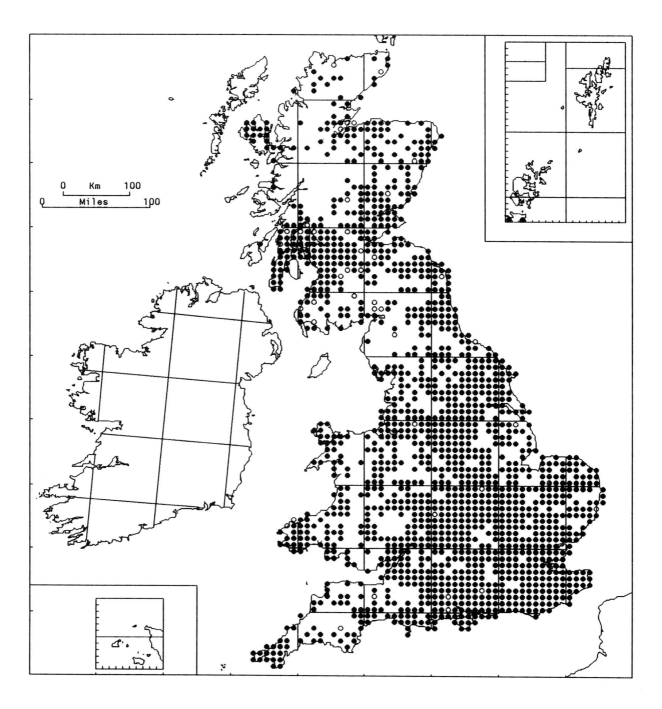

● 1960 onwards   (Great Britain 1490, Channel Islands 0)

○ Up to 1959   (Great Britain 41, Channel Islands 0)

Weasel (*Mustela nivalis* L. 1766)

Handbook 387-396.

Status Native. Common.

Protection status BC Appendix III.

Description and recognition The weasel is a small long-bodied carnivore with a short (20-30% head and body length) tail that has no black tip. Generally smaller than the stoat (although there may be size overlap with large male weasels and young female stoats), the weasel has a more sandy-brown coat.

Out of a total of 3640 records, 2576 include details of the nature of the record:

Sight	1896	(73.6%)
Museum specimen	154	(6.0%)
Road casualty	152	(5.9%)
Found dead	140	(5.4%)
Killed	135	(5.2%)
Cat kill	24	(0.9%)
Bird pellet	17	(0.7%)

There is a spring peak in sightings which may relate to increased activity during the mating period (Figure 36), whilst non-sighting records peak in April and August (Figure 37).

Figure 36. Total number of sight records of weasels for each month

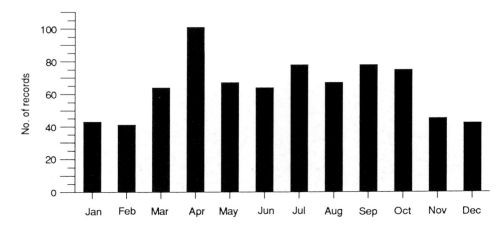

Figure 37. Total number of records, other than sightings, of weasels for each month

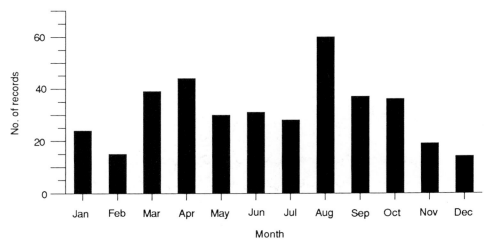

Polecat

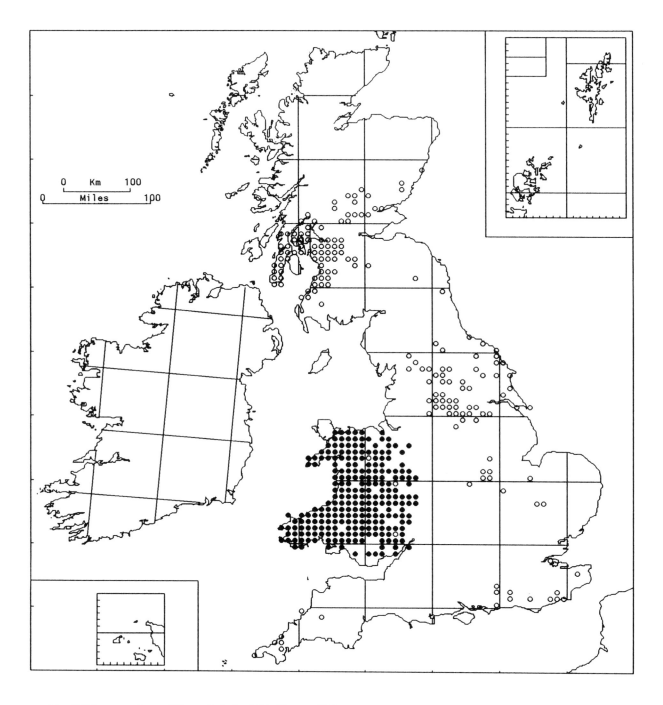

● 1960 onwards   (Great Britain 235, Channel Islands 0)

○ Up to 1959   (Great Britain 174, Channel Islands 0)

Polecat (*Mustela putorius* L. 1758)

Handbook 396-405.

Status Native. Common where it occurs. Increasing.

Protection status WCA Schedule 6. BC Appendix III.

Description and recognition The polecat is a medium sized, long-bodied mustelid carnivore with distinctive black and white facial markings. It is very difficult to distinguish from dark-coated feral ferrets.

The polecat is now spreading from Wales, although it is extremely unlikely that it will regain all the ground it has lost since 1800. Confusion and hybridisation with escaped or feral ferrets will make it difficult to keep track of any large-scale spread beyond the counties bordering Wales, but it is likely that this spread will continue, given that it is now partly protected under the Wildlife and Countryside Act. Most of the pre-1960 records outside the main range are from the 19th century. Only 29 of these 10 km squares have 20th century records and, of these, only eight are later than 1930.

Out of a total of 1385 records, 1087 include details of the nature of the record:

Road casualty	408	(37.5%)
Sight	278	(25.6%)
Killed	262	(24.1%)
Found dead	73	(6.7%)
Museum specimen	24	(2.2%)

Records peak in April and September (Figure 38). The spring peak is when the males are sexually active, and the autumn peak is when the young are recruited to the population. Records of road casualties peak strongly in September-October (Figure 39) which probably reflects high mortality in young animals. Few polecats are reported trapped or shot in June and July (Figure 40) when the young are in the nest.

Figure 38. Total number of records of polecats for each month

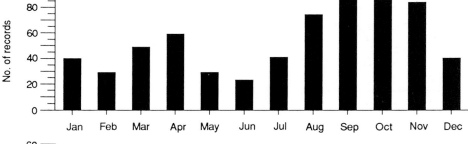

Figure 39. Total number of road casualty records of polecats for each month

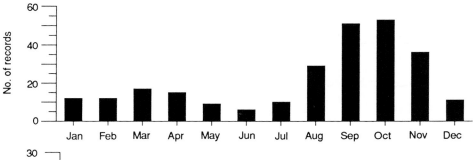

Figure 40. Total number of records of polecats killed for each month

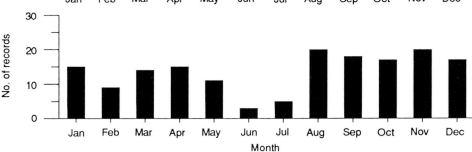

Feral ferret

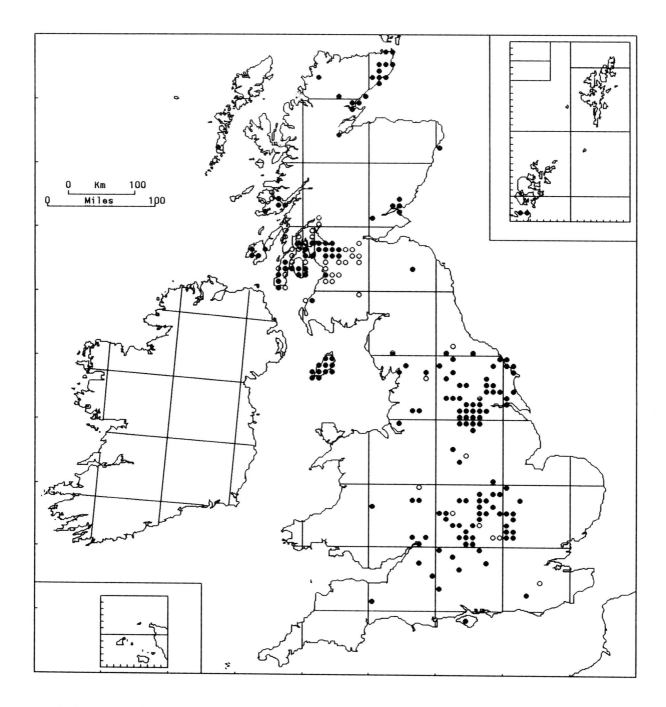

● 1960 onwards   (Great Britain 177, Channel Islands 0)

○ Up to 1959   (Great Britain 43, Channel Islands 0)

Feral ferret (*Mustela furo* L. 1758)

Handbook 405-406.

Status Introduced. Only
established on a few
islands.

Protection status

Description and recognition The ferret is often very similar to the
polecat, but there are also many albino or pale-coated animals.

The distribution and status of feral ferrets in Britain are far from clear.
There is a wide scatter of records on the mainland, but it is doubtful
whether many, if any, of these refer to self-perpetuating populations. On
the Isle of Man and on Mull, however, they do breed in the wild.

Out of a total of 317 records, 180 include details of the nature of the
record:

Sight	63	(35.0%)
Road casualty	33	(18.3%)
Museum specimen	32	(17.8%)
Found dead	26	(14.4%)
Killed	21	(11.7%)

Ferrets seem to escape very frequently, and there are certainly many
unreported sightings.

Mink

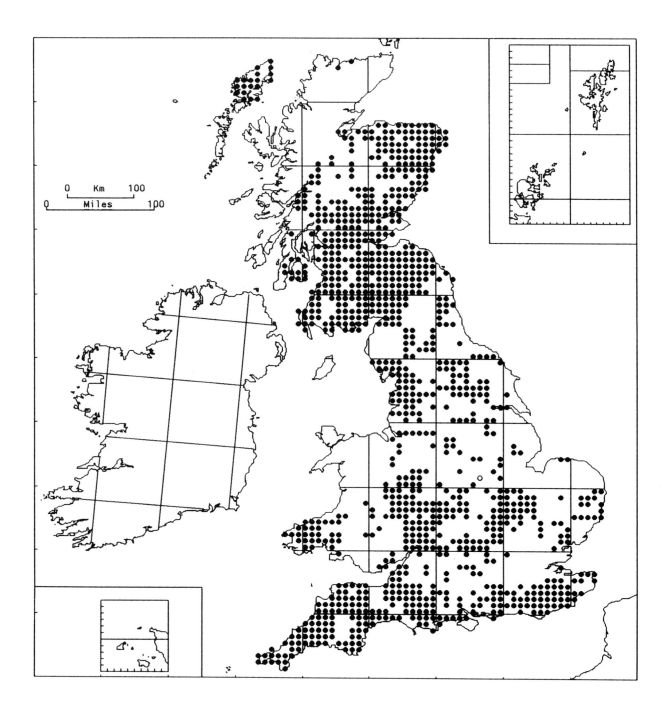

● 1960 onwards   (Great Britain 1051, Channel Islands 0)

○ Up to 1959   (Great Britain 1, Channel Islands 0)

Mink (*Mustela vison* Schreber 1777)

Handbook 406-415.

Status Introduced. Ireland - Introduced. Widespread except in the north and west.

Protection status

Description and recognition The mink is a medium-sized, long-bodied, mustelid carnivore, usually with dark-brown fur and a white chin. It has a somewhat bushy tail about half the length of the head and body.

Introduced from North America to fur farms in the 1930s, mink soon escaped and became established in the wild. They are now to be found in many parts of the country, and seem likely to continue spreading. Although derived from captive animals which are bred to have a wide variety of coat colours, most wild mink have a dark-brown coat. Many of the records for this species come from published surveys of otters, as mink or their signs are frequently encountered during otter survey work. These survey records are usually without details.

Out of a total of 2468 records, 1058 include details of the nature of the record:

Killed	459	(43.4%)
Sight	215	(20.3%)
Tracks	163	(15.4%)
Faeces	148	(14.0%)
Museum specimen	24	(2.3%)
Found dead	22	(2.1%)
Road casualty	17	(1.6%)

As for many of the other carnivores, the number of records for mink peaks in spring and autumn (Figure 41), but the peak for mink is in March, reflecting the slightly earlier mating season of this species.

Figure 41. Total number of records of mink for each month

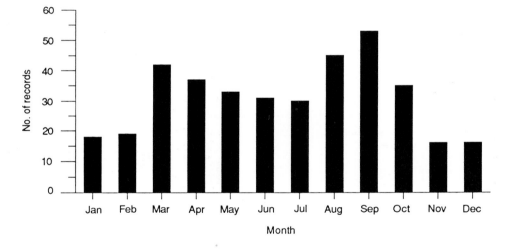

Badger

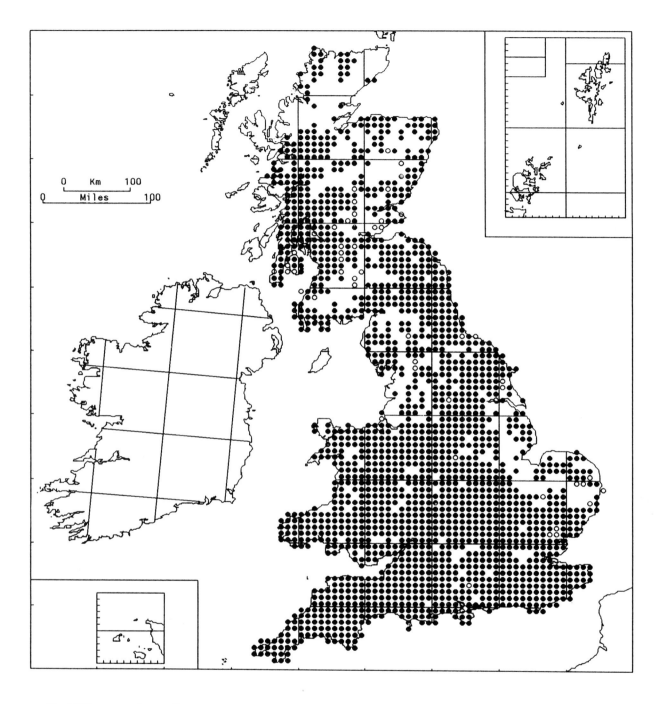

● 1960 onwards   (Great Britain 1800, Channel Islands 0)

○ Up to 1959   (Great Britain 51, Channel Islands 0)

Badger (*Meles meles* (L. 1785))

Handbook 415-423.

Status Native. Common. Ireland - common and widespread.

Protection status WCA Schedule 6. Various Badger Acts. BC Appendix III.

Description and recognition The grey body fur and black-and-white striped head make the badger easy to identify.

The badger has been the subject of several surveys in the past 20 years. The most recent (Cresswell, Harris & Jefferies 1990) reveals that populations are generally larger than at the turn of the century, although in some areas they are apparently threatened by such factors as badger digging.

Out of a total of 5484 records, 4042 include details of the nature of the record:

Setts	2365	(58.5%)
Sight	692	(17.1%)
Road casualty	378	(9.4%)
Tracks	178	(4.4%)
Found dead	124	(3.1%)
Killed	94	(2.3%)
Faeces	90	(2.2%)
Museum specimen	81	(2.0%)

Road casualties peak in March, July and October (Figure 42), and this pattern is broadly similar to that reported by Jefferies (1975) but there is no information in these records to separate mortality by sexes. Jefferies suggests that the spring peak is due mainly to sexually active males making longer journeys at this time; that the summer peak may be due to females becoming more active after having weaned their cubs; and that the autumn peak may be due to a general increase in dispersal activity of both sexes. There is no spring peak in sightings of badgers (Figure 43).

Figure 42. Total number of road casualty records of badgers for each month

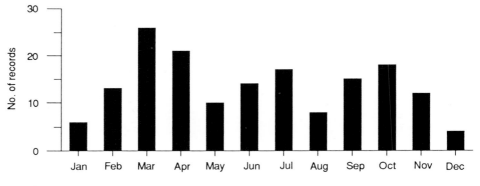

Figure 43. Total number of sight records of badgers for each month

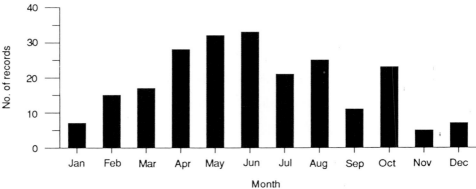

The small number of records in December and January reflects the low level of badger activity outside the setts at this time of year.

Otter

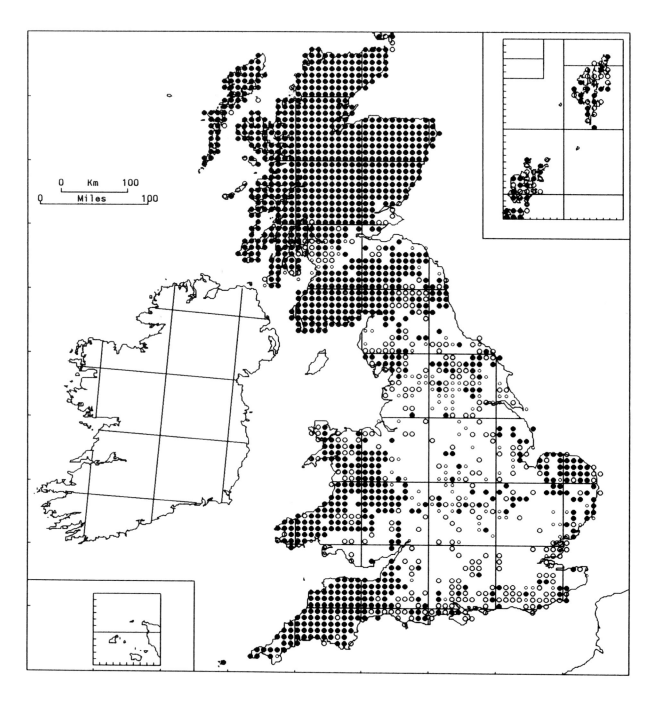

● 1975 onwards   (Great Britain 1308, Channel Islands 0)

○ 1960–1974 incl.   (Great Britain 348, Channel Islands 0)

o Up to 1959   (Great Britain 119, Channel Islands 0)

Otter (*Lutra lutra* (L. 1758))

Handbook 424-431.

Status Native.
Endangered in England and Wales; vulnerable in Scotland. Has declined. Ireland - widely distributed.

Protection status WCA Schedule 5, 6. BC Appendix II.

Description and recognition The otter is a large, long-bodied carnivore with a broad muzzle and tapering tail.

The otter has been the subject of several surveys over the past 15 years (eg Crawford *et al.* 1979; Lenton, Chanin & Jefferies 1980; Green & Green 1980; Andrews & Crawford 1986; Strachan *et al.* 1990), and its distribution is now well known. Observers need to be careful to avoid confusion with the introduced American mink, which will be seen in similar aquatic habitats to the otter. The presence of otters is most often detected by their droppings (spraints) which have a characteristic, not unpleasant, smell, different from that of mink scats.

Out of a total of 4297 records, 2090 include details of the nature of the record:

Faeces	951	(45.5%)
Sight	661	(31.6%)
Tracks	162	(7.8%)
Hunt record	118	(5.6%)
Museum specimen	59	(2.8%)
Found dead	41	(2.0%)
Road casualty	39	(1.9%)

Although apparently now increasing in the south-west of England, it is very uncommon in eastern and southern England and almost absent from the central region. In Wales and Scotland the situation is much better, although it appears that the population on Anglesey declined to a very low level in the early 1980s (Andrews & Crawford 1986). It is found on many islands.

There is a peak in the number of records collected in May, with a smaller peak in August (Figure 44).

Figure 44. Total number of records of otters for each month

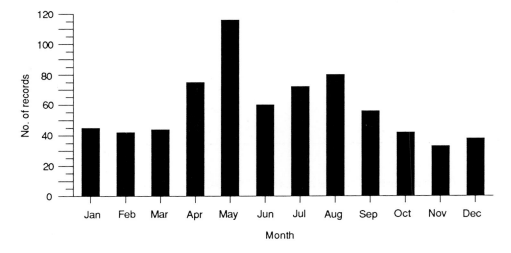

Wildcat

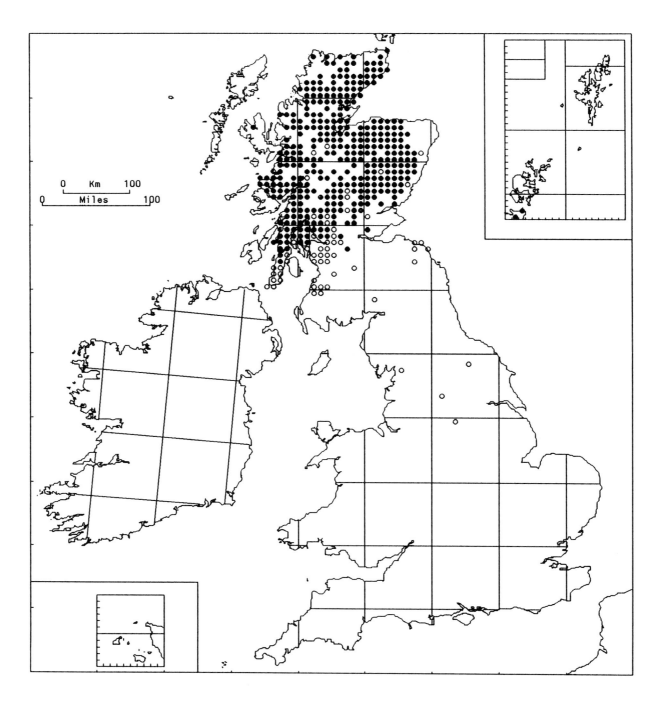

● 1960 onwards   (Great Britain 347, Channel Islands 0)

○ Up to 1959   (Great Britain 59, Channel Islands 0)

Wildcat (*Felis sylvestris* Schreber 1777)

Handbook 431-437.

Status Native. Uncommon; low density. Increasing range.

Protection status WCA Schedule 5, 6. BC Appendix III.

Description and recognition This animal is a large, robust 'tabby' cat which can be difficult to distinguish from domestic or feral tabby cats, although the tail of the wildcat tends to be less tapering and has a blunt end. The situation is further confused by hybridisation of wildcats with feral or domestic cats, and it is likely that only isolated populations remain pure. What effect hybridisation will have on the species is not known.

A recent survey (Easterbee, Hepburn & Jefferies 1991) has clarified the current distribution of this species.

Out of a total of 693 records, 267 include details of the nature of the record:

Museum specimen	130	(48.7%)
Sight	84	(31.5%)
Killed	21	(7.9%)
Trapped	11	(4.1%)

The pre-1960 records are almost all 19th century or earlier. The only English 20th century record is from Hutton Roof in 1922, where two cats were seen. One was shot and preserved and the identification seems to be genuine, although no detailed measurements of the specimen have been traced. Forestry plantations have probably helped the wildcat spread from the nadir it reached in the early part of this century. At present, the industrialised belt from Glasgow to Edinburgh appears to be acting as an effective barrier to any further spread southwards.

Common seal

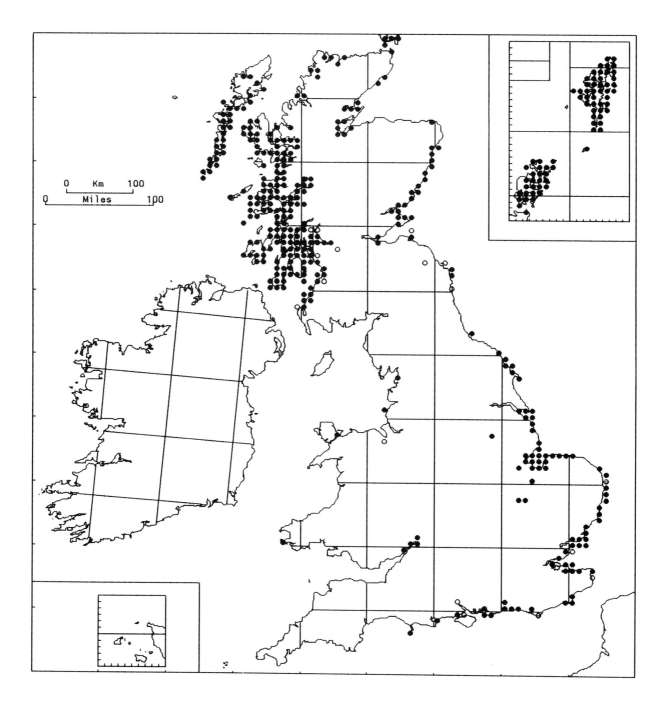

● 1960 onwards   (Great Britain 387, Channel Islands 0)

○ Up to 1959   (Great Britain 16, Channel Islands 0)

Common seal (*Phoca vitulina* L. 1758)

Handbook 462-471.

Status Native. Locally common; small population overall. Increasing? Ireland - occurs all round the coast but does not breed in south or south-east.

Protection status Conservation of Seals Act 1970. BC Appendix III.

Description and recognition It is not easy to separate the common seal from the grey seal. Common seals have a rounder head and concave forehead, and the nostrils almost meet in a 'V' shape.

Common seals prefer shallow waters and are usually observed hauled out on sandbanks and mudflats. They occasionally swim up rivers and the large population in the Wash has given rise to several inland records. The records in square TL are of seals which swam up the River Ouse as far as St Ives and Godmanchester. One actually gave birth at St Ives (date uncertain). The record at TF40 is from the River Nene at Guyhirn. The record at SK87 refers to a seal which swam up the River Witham. A large number of the records have come from the Sea Mammal Research Unit at Cambridge.

Out of a total of 560 records, 193 include details of the nature of the record:

Sight	161	(83.4%)
Found dead	23	(11.9%)
Museum specimen	3	(1.6%)

Of the dated records, higher numbers come in the summer when pupping occurs (Figure 45).

Figure 45. Total number of records of common seals for each month

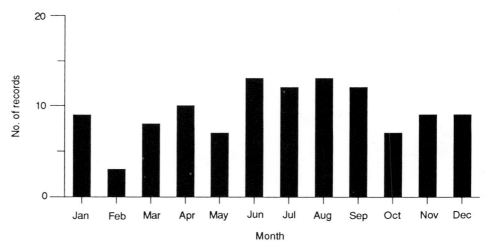

Month

Grey seal

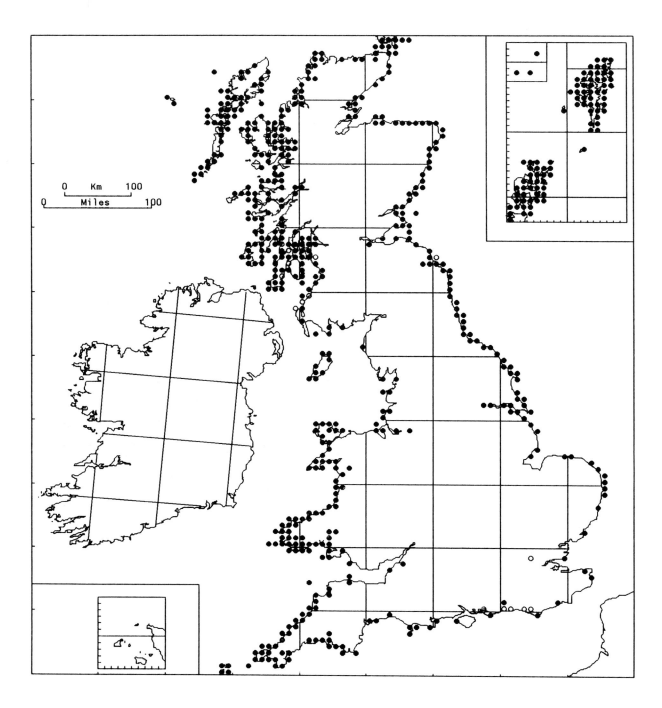

● 1960 onwards   (Great Britain 561, Channel Islands 0)

○ Up to 1959   (Great Britain 14, Channel Islands 0)

Grey seal (*Halichoerus grypus* (Fabricius 1791))

Handbook 471-480.

Status Native. Locally common; rare internationally. Increasing. Ireland - breeds on most of the coast except the south-east.

Protection status Conservation of Seals Act 1970. BC Appendix III.

Description and recognition The grey seal has an elongated muzzle and a straight or convex forehead. The nostrils are almost parallel and do not meet at the base.

The grey seal is usually found on rocky coasts and islets, sometimes in very exposed areas. A large number of the records have come from the Sea Mammal Research Unit at Cambridge.

Out of a total of 884 records, 453 include details of the nature of the record:

Sight	413	(91.2%)
Found dead	27	(6.0%)
Museum specimen	7	(1.5%)

The numbers of records peak in late spring and in autumn (Figure 46). The autumn peak is probably related to pupping, which occurs then.

Figure 46. Total number of records of grey seals for each month

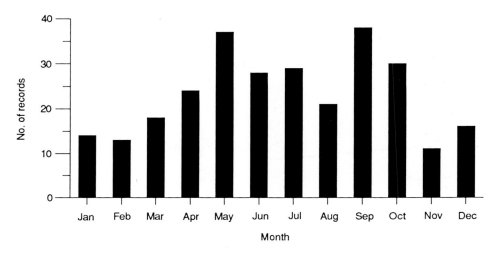

About 50% of the world population of grey seals breeds in Britain.

Red deer

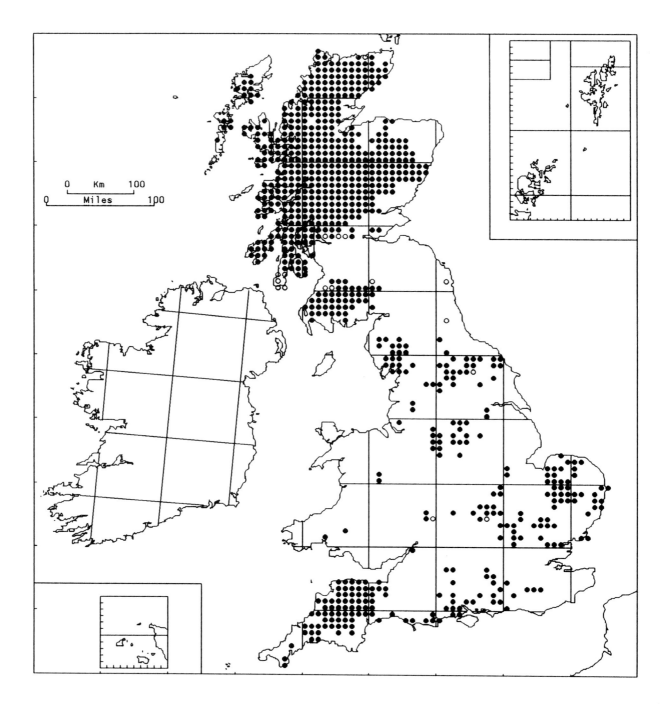

● 1960 onwards   (Great Britain 783, Channel Islands 0)

○ Up to 1959   (Great Britain 18, Channel Islands 0)

Red deer (*Cervus elaphus* L. 1758)

Handbook 492-504.

Status Native. Common. Has increased. Ireland - a few herds; present in the north, south-east and south-west. Mostly introduced.

Protection status Various Deer Acts. BC Appendix III.

Description and recognition This is a large (up to 120 cm shoulder height) deer with a red-brown coat. It has no black markings on its rump or tail.

In much of Scotland and in south-west England, red deer are animals of open moorland, but elsewhere they are found in woodland, especially in young conifer plantations. They can cause damage to young trees and prevent regeneration.

Out of a total of 1392 records, 1138 include details of the nature of the record:

Sight	1076	(94.6%)
Museum specimen	21	(1.8%)
Tracks	13	(1.1%)
Killed	11	(1.0%)

Sika deer

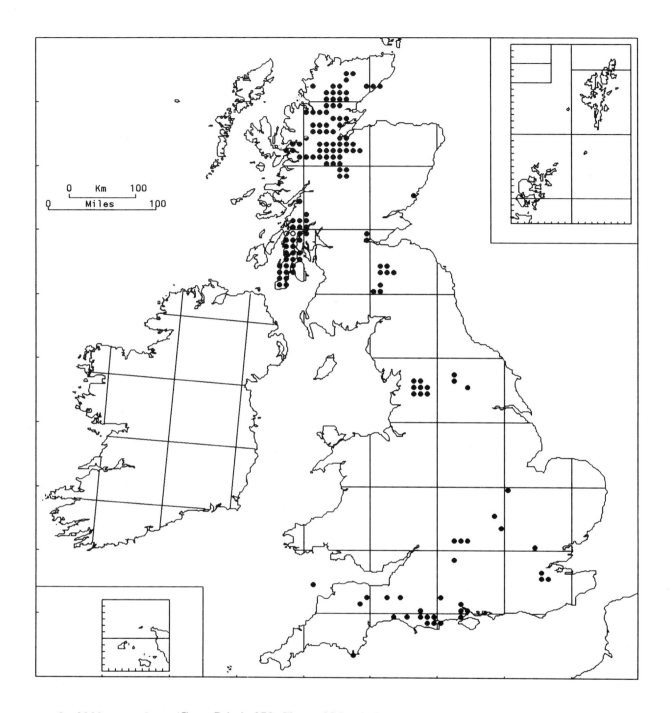

● 1960 onwards   (Great Britain 153, Channel Islands 0)

○ Up to 1959   (Great Britain 2, Channel Islands 0)

Sika deer (*Cervus nippon* Temminck 1838)

Handbook 504-508.

Status Introduced; several introductions between 1860 and 1920. Common. Ireland - introduced; occurs in the north, east, and south-west.

Protection status Various Deer Acts. BC Appendix III.

Description and recognition The sika is a medium-sized deer (85 cm shoulder height) with a lightly spotted coat, reddish-brown in summer and grey-black in winter. It has a white rump patch edged with black, and non-palmate antlers.

All wild populations are the result of escapes from parks or deliberate releases. In some areas hybridisation occurs with red deer, and concern has been expressed that this may seriously affect native red deer stocks.

Fallow deer

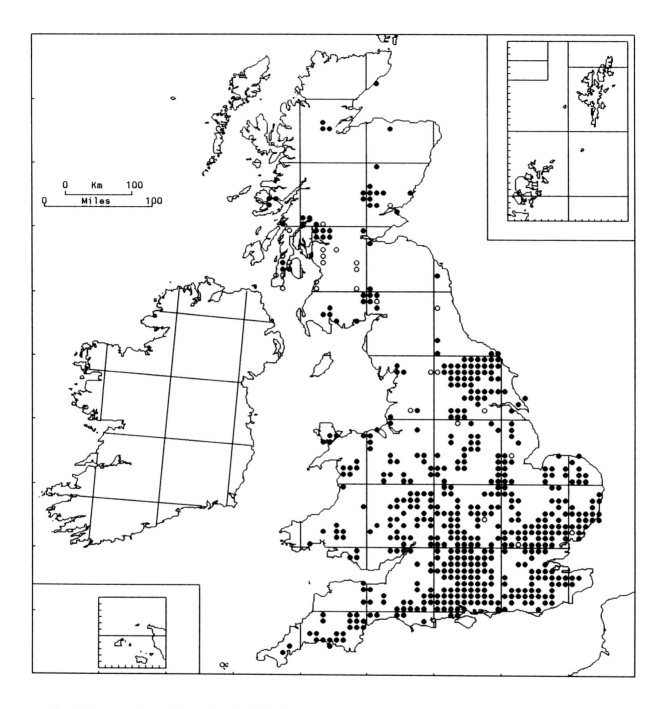

● 1960 onwards   (Great Britain 546, Channel Islands 0)

○ Up to 1959   (Great Britain 30, Channel Islands 0)

Fallow deer (*Dama dama* (L. 1758))

Handbook 509-518.

Status Introduced, probably in the 11th century. Common. Ireland - introduced; quite widespread, especially in the central area.

Protection status Various Deer Acts. BC Appendix III.

Description and recognition The fallow are medium-sized (90 cm shoulder height) deer with a wide variety of coat colours, but the typical summer coat is fawn with white spots. Sika can be similar but their spots are less apparent and they have shorter tails. Male fallow have palmate antlers, whereas sika antlers are not palmate.

Introduced into Britain by the Normans, fallow deer have escaped from many enclosed park herds and there are several population centres. They prefer mature deciduous or mixed woodland (Chapman & Putman 1991).

Out of a total of 992 records, 673 include details of the nature of the record:

Sight	602	(89.5%)
Tracks	31	(4.6%)
Killed	8	(1.2%)
Museum specimen	8	(1.2%)
Road casualty	8	(1.2%)

Roe deer

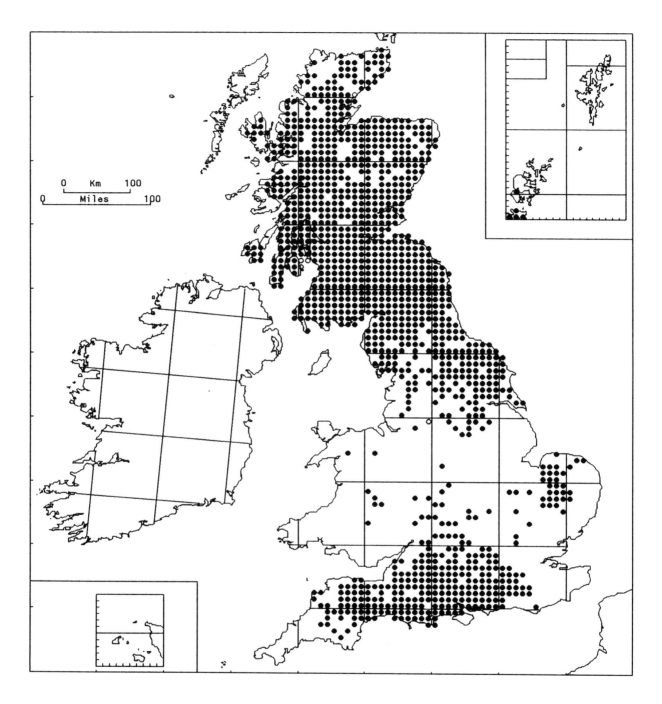

● 1960 onwards   (Great Britain 1237, Channel Islands 0)

○ Up to 1959   (Great Britain 5, Channel Islands 0)

Roe deer (*Capreolus capreolus* L. 1758)

Handbook 518-525.

Status Native, but southern English populations introduced from Scotland and Europe. Common. Increasing.

Protection status Various Deer Acts. BC Appendix III.

Description and recognition This medium-sized deer has a very short tail and pale rump patch. The male has short antlers.

Roe are primarily a woodland species. In Scotland they have spread since the early 19th century, when populations were at a low level, benefitting from the increase in woodland available.

Out of a total of 2599 records, 2065 include details of the nature of the record:

Sight	1895	(91.8%)
Tracks	61	(3.0%)
Museum specimen	42	(2.0%)
Killed	23	(1.1%)

Roe deer occur on a few of the larger islands in the Inner Hebrides and the Clyde islands; in 1989 a broken skull was found on the beach at Warbeth on Orkney mainland.

Muntjac

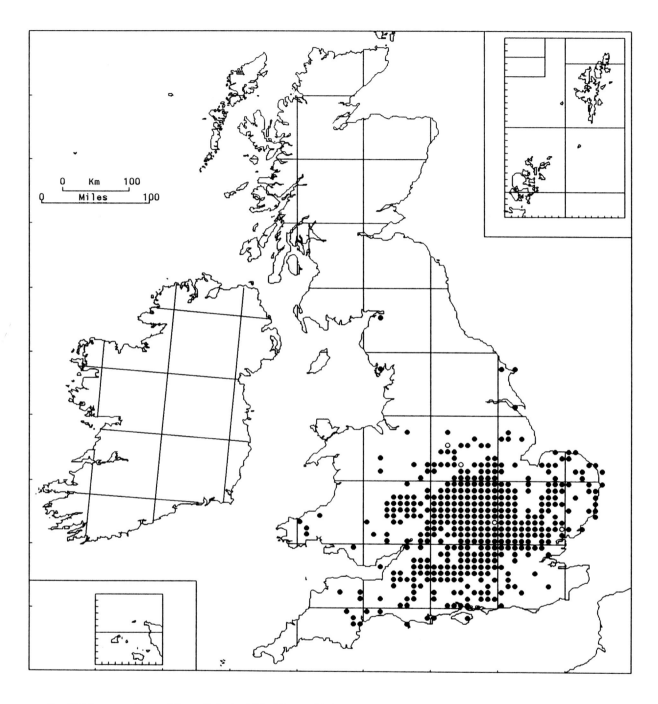

● 1960 onwards   (Great Britain 417, Channel Islands 0)

○ Up to 1959   (Great Britain 4, Channel Islands 0)

Muntjac (*Muntiacus reevesi* (Ogilby 1839))

Handbook 526-532.

Status Introduced; escaped from Woburn Park, Bedfordshire in the early 1920s. Common where it occurs. Increasing.

Protection status Various Deer Acts. BC Appendix III.

Description and recognition The muntjac is a small (50 cm shoulder height) deer with a rich chestnut-brown coat in summer, rather duller in winter. It has a long tail which is white underneath and covers a white rump patch. When alarmed, the tail is raised and the white patch and white underside of the tail are very visible. Males have short, simple antlers which arise from pedicles on the skull.

The muntjac prefers dense vegetation, and its size allows it to utilise small areas of habitat, such as copses, thickets, neglected gardens and even overgrown hedgerows. Its small size allows it to hide in low undergrowth and it may go unnoticed for some while when it colonises a new locality. It has spread rapidly since its introduction, and continues to do so.

Out of a total of 1352 records, 578 include details of the nature of the record:

Sight	465	(80.4%)
Tracks	40	(6.9%)
Road casualty	28	(4.8%)
Killed	14	(2.4%)
Found dead	7	(1.2%)
Museum specimen	7	(1.2%)

Muntjac do not have a defined breeding season as females have a seven-month gestation period and come into season immediately after giving birth; hence, young may be born at any time of year.

Chinese water deer

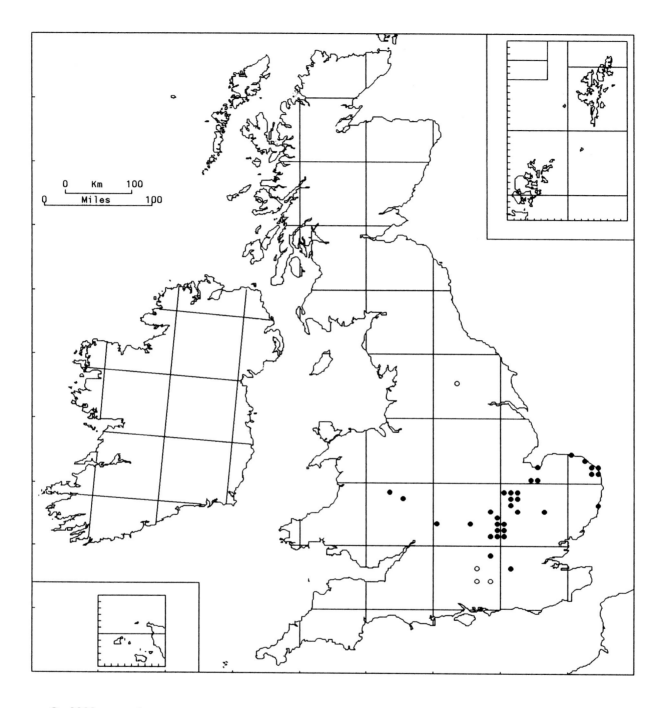

● 1960 onwards   (Great Britain 33, Channel Islands 0)

○ Up to 1959   (Great Britain 4, Channel Islands 0)

Chinese water deer (*Hydropotes inermis* Swinhoe 1870)

Handbook 532-537.

Status Introduced; escaped from parks in the middle of this century. Uncommon and local.

Protection status Various Deer Acts. BC Appendix III.

Description and recognition The Chinese water deer is small (60 cm shoulder height), and is sometimes confused with the muntjac. It has large rounded ears, and a short tail. Neither sex has antlers, but adult males have large, prominent upper canines.

Although Chinese water deer have been introduced to several parks throughout Britain, and many escapes have occurred, they have only become established around three main population centres: Whipsnade Park in Bedfordshire, Woodwalton Fen NNR in Cambridgeshire, and the Norfolk Broads. The Cambridgeshire and Norfolk wetlands are presumably somewhat similar in structure to their native habitats in China and Korea, but the Bedfordshire population survives in parkland and woodland, with regular additions escaping from Whipsnade Park where there is a free-living population within the park boundary.

Feral goat

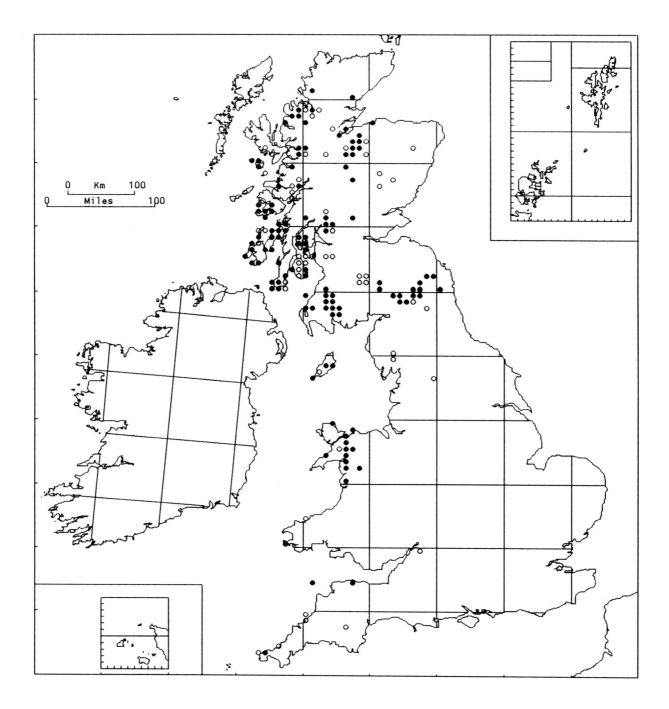

● 1960 onwards   (Great Britain 116, Channel Islands 0)

○ Up to 1959   (Great Britain 56, Channel Islands 0)

Feral goat (*Capra hircus* L. 1758)

Handbook 541-547.

Status Introduced some 5000 years ago. Ireland - introduced; scattered herds.

Protection status

Description and recognition Feral goats have long hair, varying in colour from white to black, through shades and patches of grey and brown. They are usually horned.

Out of a total of 340 records, 141 include details of the nature of the record:

Sight	137	(97.2%)
Found dead	3	(2.1%)
Shot	1	(0.7%)

Feral goat herds are found mainly in mountainous areas in Wales and Scotland, and on a few islands. Some herds are threatened by trophy hunters, and some are regarded as pests to forestry and agriculture and are subject to culling. Mild winters allow greater survival of the young, and hence population increases.

Acknowledgements

This *Atlas* would not have been possible without the help of the many people who spent time filling in record cards, and I am especially grateful to those county recorders who collated records from many field workers. The Mammal Society set up the survey, and I owe a great debt to Dr G B Corbet who organised it in the early years and is responsible for much of its success.

I am also very grateful to my colleagues past and present at the Biological Records Centre for their support and assistance. Paul Harding, the head of BRC, deserves special mention for his guidance, as does Wendy Forrest who undertook much of the data entry.

References

Andrews, E. & Crawford, A.K. 1986. *Otter survey of Wales 1984-85*. London: Vincent Wildlife Trust.

Arnold, H.R. 1978. *Provisional atlas of the mammals of the British Isles*. Abbots Ripton: Biological Records Centre.

Arnold, H.R. 1984. *Distribution maps of the mammals of the British Isles*. Abbots Ripton: Biological Records Centre.

Baker, S.J. 1986. Free-living golden hamsters (*Mesocricetus auratus*) in London. *Journal of Zoology A*, **209**, 285-286.

Baker, S.J. 1990. Escaped exotic mammals in Britain. *Mammal Review*, **20**, 75-96.

Brockie, R.E. 1960. Road mortality of the hedgehog (*Erinaceus europaeus* L.) in New Zealand. *Proceedings of the Zoological Society of London*, **134**, 505-508.

Chapman, N.G. & Putman, R.J. 1991. Fallow deer. In: *The handbook of British mammals*, edited by G.B. Corbet & S. Harris, 3rd ed., 508-518. Oxford: Mammal Society.

Cooper, M.E. 1987. *An introduction to animal law*. London: Academic Press.

Corbet, G.B. 1971. Provisional distribution maps of British mammals. *Mammal Review*, **1**, 95-142.

Corbet, G.B. & Harris, S., eds. 1991. *The handbook of British mammals*. 3rd ed. Oxford: Blackwell Scientific for the Mammal Society.

Corbet, G.B. & Southern, H.N., eds. 1977. *The handbook of British mammals*. 2nd ed. Oxford: Blackwell Scientific for the Mammal Society.

Crawford, A., Evans, D., Jones, A. & McNulty, J. 1979. *Otter survey of Wales 1977-78*. Lincoln: Society for the Promotion of Nature Conservation.

Cresswell, P., Harris, S. & Jefferies, D.J. 1990. *The history, distribution, status and habitat requirements of the badger in Britain*. Peterborough: Nature Conservancy Council.

Easterbee, N., Hepburn, L.V. & Jefferies, D.J. 1991. *Survey of the status and distribution of the wildcat in Scotland, 1983-1987*. Edinburgh: Nature Conservancy Council for Scotland.

Fargher, S.E. 1977. The distribution of the brown hare (*Lepus capensis*) and the mountain hare (*Lepus timidus*) in the Isle of Man. *Journal of Zoology*, **182**, 164-167.

Flowerdew, J.R. 1984. *Wood mice and yellow-necked mice*. (Mammal Society Series.) Oswestry: Nelson.

Ford, C.E. & Hamerton, J.L. 1970. Chromosome polymorphism in the common shrew, *Sorex araneus*. *Symposia of the Zoological Society of London*, **26**, 223-236.

Gibson, J.A. 1973. The distribution of voles on the Clyde Islands. *The Western Naturalist*, **2**, 40-43.

Goransson, G. & Carlson, J. 1982. Hunting and road mortality in the pheasant and the European hare in southern Sweden. *Transactions of the 14th Congress of the International Union of Game Biologists, Dublin, 1979*, 343-349.

Gosling, L.M. & Baker, S.J. 1989. The eradication of muskrats and coypus from Britain. *Biological Journal of the Linnean Society*, **38**, 39-51.

Green, J., & Green, R. 1980. *Otter survey of Scotland 1977-79*. London: Vincent Wildlife Trust.

Harris, S. 1979. History, distribution, status and habitat requirements of the harvest mouse (*Micromys minutus*) in Britain. *Mammal Review*, **9**, 159-171.

Harris, S. & Jefferies, D.J. 1991. Working within the law: guidelines for veterinary surgeons and wildlife rehabilitators on the rehabilitation of wild mammals. *British Veterinary Journal*, **147**, 1-17.

Harvie-Brown, J.A. & Buckley, T.E. 1892. *A vertebrate fauna of Argyll and the Inner Hebrides*. Edinburgh: David Douglas.

Hill, J.E. & Yalden, D.W. 1990. The status of the hoary bat, *Lasiurus cinereus*, as a British species. *Journal of Zoology*, **222**, 694-697.

Howes, C.A. 1984. Free-range gerbils. *Bulletin of the Yorkshire Naturalists Union,* **1**, 10.

Jefferies, D.J. 1975. Different activity patterns of male and female badgers (*Meles meles*) as shown by road mortality. *Journal of Zoology,* **177**, 504-506.

Jefferies, D.J. & Mitchell-Jones, A.J. 1989. Mammals. In: *Guidelines for selection of biological SSSIs,* 232-241. Peterborough: Nature Conservancy Council.

Jenkins, P.D. 1977. Water shrew. In: *The handbook of British mammals,* edited by G.B.Corbet & H.N. Southern, 2nd ed., 57-61. Oxford: Blackwell Scientific for the Mammal Society.

Kutzer, E. & Frey, H. 1981. Effects of road traffic on hares. *Proceedings of the World Lagomorph Conference, 1979,* 501-507. Ontario: University of Guelph.

Lenton, E.J., Chanin, P.R.F. & Jefferies, D.J. 1980. *Otter survey of England 1977-79.* Shrewsbury: Nature Conservancy Council.

Lever, C. 1979. *The naturalized animals of the British Isles.* London: Granada Publishing.

Meylan, A. & Hausser, J. 1978. Le type chromosomique A des *Sorex* du groupe *araneus*: *Sorex coronatus* Millet, 1828 (Mammalia,Insectivora)(*). *Mammalia,* **42**, 115-122.

Ni Lamhna, E. 1979. *Provisional distribution atlas of amphibians, reptiles and mammals in Ireland.* Dublin: An Foras Forbartha.

Prior, R. 1983. *Trees and deer.* London: Batsford.

Sheail, J. 1988. The extermination of the muskrat (*Ondatra zibethicus*) in inter-war Britain. *Archives of Natural History,* **15**, 155-170.

Smallshire, D. & Davey, J.W. 1989. Feral Himalayan porcupines in Devon. *Nature in Devon,* **10**, 62-69.

Stebbings, R.E. 1989. The Bechstein's bat (*Myotis bechsteinii*) in Dorset and Britain 1800-1989. *Proceedings of the Dorset Natural History and Archaeological Society,* **110**, 178-180.

Stebbings, R.E. & Arnold, H.R. 1990. Preliminary observations of 20th century changes in the distribution and status of *Rhinolophus ferrumequinum* in Britain. In: *European Bat Research 1987,* edited by V.Hanek, I. Horacek & J. Gaisler, 559-563. Praha: Charles University Press.

Strachan, R., Birks, J.D.S., Chanin, P.R.F. & Jefferies, D.J. 1990. *Otter survey of England 1984-1986.* Peterborough: Nature Conservancy Council.

Tapper, S.C. & Parsons, N. 1984. The changing status of the brown hare (*Lepus capensis* L.) in Britain. *Mammal Review,* **14**, 57-70.

Twigg, G.I. 1992. The black rat *Rattus rattus* in the United Kingdom in 1989. *Mammal Review,* **22**, 33-42.

Velander, K.A. 1983. *Pine marten survey of England, Scotland and Wales 1980-1982.* London: Vincent Wildlife Trust.

Warwick, T. 1940. A contribution to the ecology of the musk-rat (*Ondatra zibethica*) in the British Isles. *Proceedings of the Zoological Society of London A,* **110**, 165-201.